The Memorial *of* Jesus

Stories Told by the Disciples
Who Called Him *Friend*

Judy Jeub

Edited by Kellie Hultgren
ISBN 13: 978-1-59298-664-4
Library of Congress Catalog Number: 2018903617
Printed in the United States of America
First Printing: 2018
22 21 20 19 18   5 4 3 2 1
Book design and typesetting by Laura Drew.
Cover photo of Mount Tabor © shutterstock/olegsubaru

Beaver's Pond Press
7108 Ohms Lane
Edina, MN 55439–2129
(952) 829-8818
www.BeaversPondPress.com
To order, visit www.JudyJeub.com.

This project was made possible by a grant provided by the Five Wings Art Council with funds from the McKnight Foundation.

To the awakened ones, and to those
waiting to be awakened.

TABLE OF CONTENTS

PREFACE

In August 2014, my husband and I attended a memorial service for John Huebsch, a remarkable man, who had died unexpectedly of a heart attack at only fifty-three years old while chopping wood outside his friend's cabin in central Minnesota. John had been the executive director for Common Hope, an organization that serves the poor of Guatemala, where my husband and I had gone several times with work teams. John is as close to my idea of a saint as anyone I have ever met.

The service, which took place in Minneapolis about a month after John's death, was a beautiful reunion for those who had served at Common Hope. After a ritual of readings and sacred song, family and friends were invited to come forward to share their most cherished memories of John. The stories they told were not about the important work he had done for Common Hope. Rather, they shared intimate recollections of John as brother, nephew, friend, and coworker.

His sister told a story about the time she lied about her brother hitting her, and how their father picked up a hammer and destroyed the little house John was building. "This is what you do to your brothers and sisters when you hurt them! We are here to build up, not to tear down!"

One of his coworkers told us about the time he borrowed a pencil from John, and then proceeded to lose the pencil. He was dismayed when John expected the pencil to be returned. "John believed in caring for God's earth by being respectful of the gifts it gives us, including pencils."

John's best friend spoke last and he shared an intimate detail that summed up what John Huebsch's life was about: "John's deepest desire was to walk through life in total consciousness of God's presence." I thought at that moment, This is what I want, too. And then I thought, This is what Jesus wanted.

As we drove home, it was difficult to speak. Something had been ignited in me and I needed to be still to let the flame grow. I know that I was realizing the power of story to reveal character, to transmit message, and to inspire change.

As a serious student and lover of the scriptures, I was always curious about what the Bible didn't say, the stories behind the recorded events. For example, the wedding feast at Cana. I wondered why Mary, when she noticed that the wine was gone, appealed to her son, Jesus, to solve the problem. Who was she to take on that responsibility? I thought. Wouldn't that have been the job of the parents of the bride and groom? I took note of the time Jesus' family members came to see him and how he disregarded them in favor of his followers. I identified with his family and felt the sting of his words. When I thought about the physical and spiritual healings, I pictured Jesus taking the time to establish relationships with those who were suffering and afraid. I questioned his always knowing what people thought and what was to come. I made notations in the margins of my Bible. Over time, those notes became stories.

I now realize that I was trying to create a more human Jesus. I was raised believing in a divine Jesus that was easy to worship but impossible to emulate. I needed a flesh-and-blood Jesus, one that could understand my struggles because he had struggled. I wanted a Jesus that found love difficult at times, even in his own family, who knew loneliness and who was hurt when he was misunderstood. I didn't want a Jesus born with divine wisdom and knowledge. I wanted someone who learned lessons through successes and failures. In my imagination, I saw a Jesus who enjoyed a good time with friends and got too smelly at his job to be welcome at his mother's table.

After John's memorial service, I came home with a new focus and a spiritual energy I had never experienced before.

I wanted to share the Jesus I had found with others through the vehicle of storytelling—and my book was born.

The first task was to select the characters. I decided to begin with those closest to Jesus, the twelve apostles. I used several sources to learn all I could about them. First, I turned to common reference books such as biblical commentaries, encyclopedias, and historic accounts. As I searched, I discovered other stories about Jesus besides those accepted into the canon. One book I found interesting and useful was *The Lost Books of the Bible*, a collection of ancient texts from the first four centuries including stories of Jesus' childhood, his trial, letters of Herod and Pilate, and accounts of the disciples as they went out into the world. Not all of these were accurate historic accounts, but the facts did not matter to me. I was not writing a biography of Jesus. I wanted to share the Jesus I had come to know and love through stories of human beings like myself.

The Nag Hammadi Scriptures is a collection of ancient texts, primarily gnostic, translated from scrolls discovered in Egypt in 1945. In it, one finds gospels written by apostles Thomas, Philip, Mary Magdalene, and Judas. Other writings are attributed to James (Yakov), the brother of Jesus, John the "Beloved Disciple," and Peter. It was in these writings that I discovered the seven women follows of Jesus. I learned that Jesus chose his brother, James, to lead the community after his death. I discovered that Mary

Magdalene was a revered leader and Jesus' confidant to whom he transmitted secret knowledge, and that Peter challenged her leadership. Thomas and Matthew, on the other hand, supported her.

Reading these ancient texts, some dating back as early as the first cenutry CE, my mind was opened to alternative ways to interpret Jesus' message, and I am pleased to give voice to the early Christian communities these texts represent.

In the spring of 2016 I was invited to join a group traveling to Israel to take a course at St. George's College in Jerusalem. The course, "Palestine of Jesus," focused on key events in the life of Jesus, and his death and resurrection. There could not have been a more perfect opportunity for me to round out my work by actually experiencing the places where Jesus walked and preached. I was not disappointed.

Our group visited Bethlehem and Nazareth where Jesus was born and grew up. Today, these towns are bustling with business and I found it was easy to imagine the boy Jesus stopping to pester workers at the tanner's shop on his way to fetch water from the town's well. Of special interest to me was Capernaum on the north shore of Lake Galilee. There we saw the ruins of Peter's house where Jesus lived and where he and the disciples developed a plan for spreading the message about the Kingdom of God.

We took a boat on Lake Galilee and fishermen demonstrated the ancient method of catching fish by net. We traveled to the various villages along its shore where Jesus preached. On Mt. Tabor, the place of the transfiguration, I closed my eyes and, in meditation, I pictured myself with Jesus, Peter, James, and John talking about only the most important things in life. I sat on the hillside in Bethsaida where Jesus fed the crowds and I knew my soul was being fed. With my fellow travelers, I walked the narrow stone streets of Old Jerusalem, and even the path he traveled as he carried the cross. I had finally met the human Jesus.

Since a memorial service was my choice for the book's setting, I researched Jewish practices around death and bereavement. I learned about the Jewish periods of grief, including *shiva* (seven days) and *sheloshim* (one month), designed to help the loved ones through their suffering and ease them back into the life of the living. I came across a ritual performed in the synagogue, *shachrit*, that marks the end of sheloshim. This ritual is where my story begins with Jesus' priestly brother, Yakov, serving as the celebrant.

It is my hope that readers will come to realize that the Divine is revealed in the ordinary events of our lives. Each of our stories is about dying and rising, coming out of darkness into the light. Conversion is about waking up and seeing what we could not see before.

Judy Jeub
March 2018

YAKOV

I want to extend a warm welcome to all who have gathered today to remember our brother, Yeshua, or Jesus, as most of you know him. I speak for my whole family when I express gratitude for the comfort and love given to us these last few weeks. You have carried us through the terrible darkness we entered when he was so brutally tortured and hung to die. The pain still lingers, but there is light. Death is losing its grip.

You all know our mother, Mary. She and our aunt, Salome, and my sisters Mara and Salome, have made sure you and your families are well fed as we go forward with our day together. My three brothers are here: Jude, whom most of you know; my brother Joseph, who bears the name of our father and is here with his wife and children; and Simon, the youngest. They have all worked together to arrange for this beautiful place and to spread the news without alerting those who might be a danger to the community.

Sheloshim—the thirty days of mourning—have ended, and so we begin by lighting this fire in memory of our beloved. May the flame's light inspire us to live in the Kingdom into which he gathered us. May our deeds be steeped in loving kindness, our lips speak words of comfort, and our touch heal those who suffer.

See this bowl of water. Jewish tradition teaches us that we wash our hands before we embark on a sacred act so we may recognize the holy and the ordinary. We dip in the water rosemary, the herb of remembrance. With these symbols we leave sheloshim and enter a new stage of mourning by remembering.

I have invited each of the seventeen disciples to share their memories of Jesus. These are the men and women he called to join him in his mission to bring the good news of the Kingdom to our people—to all people. I asked them to speak from their hearts. We have all witnessed his works and heard his words. Today we want to remember Jesus as the child who grew up playing in the streets of Nazareth with his brothers and cousins, as the teen who challenged his parents and the rabbis, as the young man who shared stories and wine around the campfire late into the night, and as the compassionate one who sat vigil with a neighbor suffering loss.

I am pleased to have been asked to lead the service today, though I am the least worthy. I did not join my brother Yeshua in his work. I did not share his zeal, and, I am ashamed to say, I questioned his intentions. It was not until the Passover meal when he brought us together for the last time that the Spirit finally awakened me. However, it was too late. He was taken from us before I could speak to him about what had happened to my soul. But even death could not stop him from reaching out to me. It was on the eighteenth day of sheloshim he appeared. I thank Philip and Nathaniel for helping me to understand the meaning of Yeshua's words.

I wanted to choose the first speaker by lot, but the disciples elected to have Matthew begin because he is known to be a great storyteller. His wife, Arsinoe, will tell you to listen with a discerning ear. He claims to always tell the truth, but he admits to the habit of making small things large and seemingly important things frivolous. I once heard him tell a story about me, and I did not know who it was he was talking about.

Matthew, light for us a candle and share with us your memory of Jesus.

MATTHEW

I am deeply sad for you and your family, Yakov, and for Jesus' dear companion, Miriam. We have all shared in your sorrow during this time of sheloshim. But now, as you say, we must lift up our hearts to remember the good times. This is what Jesus wants.

Let me tell you the story of the day I met Jesus. It was on the fifteenth day in the month of Iyar. I remember because the day before was Pesach Sheni, a favorite holiday for Jewish tax collectors. One month after Passover, we get one more chance to eat unleavened bread and to dance and sing. There is a saying: "It is never too late even if you are a bit impure." This is what we celebrate on this little holiday.

I remember my head was hurting as I walked into the border station and saw a man planted on the bench beside the door. He said nothing, which was fine with me in my delicate situation. He just sat propped against the wall, looking at his feet.

I unpacked my record books and studied the totals I'd left from the day before. I wondered if my visitor was waiting for me to break the silence and thought perhaps this was a sign of respect. But after a while, his respect was keeping me from paying attention to the numbers. Finally I said, "Is there something you want to claim besides my bench?"

"No," he said. "I just came to show you the hole in my shoe." He held up one leg so I could see the bottom of his sandal, and just as he said, there was a sizable hole.

"That is a big hole," I said.

"Yes," he said. "It is big enough to let the stones in, and I have to keep shaking my foot to get them out. It slows me down considerably." I thought to myself that it was my leg that was being shaken. "I am not adept at using a needle and thread," he said. "I need a cobbler."

"You are in luck," I told him. "There is one on every street in Capernaum, so finding one should cause you no trouble."

"I have only a few shekels, and I hear you are an honest man. I thought you might recommend a cobbler who is both honest and inexpensive."

I laughed. "It is not easy to overcharge when there is another cobbler just a few houses away! My friend Zadock is a good man, and his work is better than most. His shop is on the second street beyond the city gate. Just turn to the right. He has a sign above his door that is shaped like a shoe, as one might expect. You will like him. He always has two stories to tell, never more, never less. But I must warn you: you have to listen to both stories, or he won't fix your shoe."

So the man left, and I thought I had seen the last of him. But near the time for me to close the office, he appeared once again at my door, this time with a grin across his face. He pointed rather proudly to his feet. "Those are fine shoes," I said. "But you were worried a cobbler would charge too much to mend the hole in your one shoe, and I see you have come from Zadock's shop with two new ones."

"Zadock told me he would repair the hole in my shoe and give the pair to some poor man who cannot afford any shoes at all. That impressed me. Zadock is a good and compassionate man."

"And a very good businessman," I added.

"Now I need to find a place to spend the night," the man said.

"You passed an inn on the way to Zadock's shop," I told him. "Did you not see it? There is a sign above the door shaped like a bed, as one might expect." He told me he had spent his last coin on the shoes, and I thought, *This man needs someone to teach him how to manage money.*

"I hear you are a man of great hospitality and your wife serves fine food," he said.

"It seems you have heard a lot of things about me," I said to him. "Yet I do not even know your name."

He told me his name was Jesus and he came from the

town of Nazareth. His mother, he said, was a widow, and her sister was Salome, wife to Zebedee who owns a fishing business in Capernaum.

"Zebedee's sons, your cousins, come through my gate often with their fish. I know the family well. You are right about my wife's cooking. Arsinoe's table is full every night. The other tax collectors like to come after work to eat her food and drink my beer. Sometimes there are also poor, hungry stragglers who have heard of her generosity. Arsinoe likes to say, 'Worries go down better with soup than without.' Come along, Jesus from Nazareth. You need to break in your new shoes."

Jesus helped me close the station, and together we walked the two and a half miles to Capernaum. When we arrived at the house, Arsinoe was already pouring beers and setting out bowls of meat and beans. I looked around to see Ammihud, a collector like myself, and Eleazer, the butcher, sitting at the table. Michtah, a woman who has no husband, was there with her young son, Simon. The boy sat under the table with one hand on his mother's lap and the other holding a piece of bread. An old woman who no longer had her wits about her sat on a chair next to the hearth. People simply call her "old woman." She is at our house for every meal. She comes and leaves without saying a word, but she always smiles at Arsinoe and touches her head in blessing as she leaves.

"This is Jesus from Nazareth," I said to Arsinoe. "He needs food to eat and a place to spend the night." My wife indicated with a wave of her ladle that the stranger should get a stool from the corner of the room. Jesus fetched it and sat himself at the table.

"Thank you, dear lady," Jesus said.

This is when Arsinoe looked up from her pot and saw him for the first time. "I know you," she said. "You are the rabbi that Perpetua and I saw teaching down by the lake earlier today." When they heard "rabbi," the other guests suddenly took notice.

Ammihud, who always enjoys a heated religious or political argument, swept his sleeve across his beard to clear the beer foam and said, "So, teacher from Nazareth, I have some questions for you. What do you think about the many laws the Pharisees say are so necessary? What is so important about how many steps a man walks on the Sabbath? Twenty? Forty? One hundred? Does a man need to carry a measuring string wherever he goes? And what does it matter whether a man touches his mezuzah as he enters and leaves his house? Sometimes a man is in a little bit of a hurry. Do you think God cares about such things?"

Jesus, scooping gravy on his bread, said, "You are a wise man, Ammihud. What God does care about is a man's intentions."

I don't think Ammihud has enough brains in his bald

head to comprehend what an intention is, but *wise* is a word not usually used to describe him, so it pleased him very much and he sat up straighter in his chair.

From that first day, Jesus fit right in and became one of my wife's frequent guests. Arsinoe especially liked him because he spoke up when the men taunted her. One day he said to Ammihud, "Arsinoe is the wife of your esteemed host, and you speak to her as though she were his slave."

Then Ammihud, embarrassed, said, "Arsinoe, esteemed wife of my esteemed friend. I ask you please to forgive me . . . while you pour me another beer." If Ammihud were twice as smart, he'd still be an idiot.

We tax collectors were pleased by Jesus' message, but not so the Pharisees, who put great importance on following the letter of the law. Some of these would come when he preached and shout accusations at him. "Jesus of Nazareth, we saw you gleaning wheat on the Sabbath as you walked with your disciples," one said. "We saw you eating an unholy food," said another.

One criticized him for eating and drinking with sinners. This did not escape me, for it was in my Arsinoe's kitchen that some of these so-called sinners gathered. Jesus said to him, "A physician comes to heal the sick, not those who are healthy." Jesus was mocking him, but the man was so proud of himself that he thought Jesus was paying him homage.

Jesus never refuted the law as he was accused. "The law that is handed down to us is not enough," he taught. He gave examples of this. "We are taught not to kill, but I say you should sweep away the anger that leads you to taking revenge on another." The law demands an eye for an eye, a tooth for a tooth, but Jesus taught us to turn the other cheek when we are offended. "Instead of retribution, God wants us to love our enemies, for they are God's children too," he said. As for the law concerning adultery, Jesus said even lusting after another woman is sin, for it is adultery of the heart.

One young Pharisee came to Jesus in private and said, "Rabbi, I am afraid if you tell people these things, they will stop following the laws and then they will fall under God's wrath."

Jesus knew the courage it took for this man to speak such words to him face-to-face. He looked at the Pharisee with compassion and said, "God is not like a judge. God is like a father. What sort of father, when his son asks for bread, would refuse him because he broke a law?"

I thought one day, as I looked upon the faces of the men and women and children who came to listen to Jesus, that when Moses first gave the law to our ancestors they were filled with fear. His words were like thunder and lightning to them. But when Jesus spoke, it was not fear they felt but hope. Moses promised to bring the people into the kingdom God would hand over to them. Jesus brought the Kingdom of God into the people, for the Kingdom dwells in the heart.

What more can I say? I miss my friend. I miss breaking bread with him. I miss the nights after our work was done when we sat under the stars and told of all we had witnessed throughout the day. And I miss his words of encouragement because today I don't feel the courage I once had.

Miriam, Jesus loved you more than any of us. You were his tower of strength. You stayed with him until the spirit left him. And now you are our tower. We appreciate the words of wisdom you always have for us even as you yourself are grieving.

Thank you, Yakov, for bringing us together on this beautiful day the Creator has given us. It is good and necessary that we turn our thoughts to the good days we had together.

YAKOV

So, Matthew, it is a worn-out shoe that brought Yeshua to your door. I can't help but wonder about the poor man who is walking around in his old shoes today . . . another story to tell, perhaps.

Your sense of Jesus' view of the law is true. I see this now, but there was great contention between my brother and I concerning the law even before he went to the East. I was startled to see he had not changed his mind after his return. He had, however, softened. He was less prone to arguing with me, making my defenses feel weak. In the long run, I suppose this led to my conversion more than anything he said. When you find yourself with no enemy to fight, you are left fighting the enemy within.

Matthew mentioned Salome, my mother's sister, who lives in Capernaum with Zebedee and their two sons, James and John. In our youth we traveled to visit our cousins who lived near the lake, a great place for mischievous boys. John was too young to participate in many of our adventures, but James was there and the leader of us all. Rightfully, where there was trouble, he was the one who took the blame.

James, along with his brother John, was among the first Jesus asked to join him in his mission. I asked him to tell us about the day the fishermen were called. Welcome, James.

JAMES, SON OF ZEBEDEE

I can still remember my bewilderment the day Matthew and Arsinoe walked into Perpetua's kitchen. Jesus greeted Matthew with a kiss and announced he had chosen him to be with us. I thought, *What does Jesus hope to accomplish by inviting a tax collector to do this work? He will drive people away, not draw them in.* I realized over time it was Arsinoe whom he had invited, and he had to take Matthew if he wanted her.

I say that with humor, for what would this journey have been without Matthew's stories? I don't know that mine will be as interesting, but it is what he has given me.

Yakov asked about the day Jesus called us to join him, so I will tell you about this first. The usual crew had gone out to fish: my brother John and I, our father Zebedee, and Peter and Andrew. Jesus had returned from the East, and we were happy to have our cousin back with us again. It was a warm day, and the surface of the lake was calm—a good day for conversing, but not so good for catching fish. We threw our nets anyway, if for no other reason than to justify our going out.

As I recall, we were talking about the Baptist's death. Andrew blamed John himself for speaking out against the authorities, but Peter defended him, saying he was a great prophet. "Would you have told Jeremiah or Isaiah to hold their tongues?" he asked.

Jesus' greatest concern, it seemed, was for John's followers. "They are like sheep who have lost their shepherd," I recall him saying.

My brother, John, bored of political talk, asked Jesus about his travels to the East. Jesus told us that while there he learned from wise men a new way of seeing the world and of understanding the Holy One. "It is very different than the way we have been taught," he said. "The teachers of the East believe that what we see with our eyes and hear with our ears is not always the truth. There is another realm they say is more real than the one we experience. This world is only a reflection of the other." Jesus called this other realm the Kingdom of God. "Yet the two are linked so that what is bound in the earthly kingdom is bound in the Heavenly Kingdom and what is loosed on Earth is loosed in Heaven." His words were meaningless to me, but John pressed him to say more.

When John asked, "Where is this Kingdom?" Jesus placed his hand on his heart and said, "It is here; it is within us."

It baffles me to this day that I chose to follow Jesus. Perhaps I was tired of the work of hauling fish, or perhaps leaving the town of my birth seemed like an adventure. More likely, I went along because it pleased me to be chosen to be a leader of sorts—this oaf of a man who could not recite the words of the Torah when he was presented in the Temple. The calling felt important, bigger than the hauling of smelly fish. "Come with me, and I will make you fishers of men," Jesus said.

In the telling of this story it is important that I share with you how I felt when Jesus included my brother John in his invitation. "He is barely a man!" my father said adamantly.

I protested as well: "John is nothing but a dreamer. He will only slow us down."

"Dreamers are closer to the Kingdom than most," Jesus said. In the end our father agreed to let John go, but only after Jesus agreed to talk to our mother. I admit I was not happy.

The first time we set out from Capernaum, there were ten of us: Jesus, Matthew and Arsinoe, and the four fishermen. Peter brought with him his wife, Priscilla, and their daughter, Petronilla. Jesus' brother Jude joined us from

Nazareth. Our numbers grew quickly, and by Yom Kippur we'd grown to fourteen, including Miriam of Bethany.

But it was only three—Peter, John, and me—whom Jesus asked to go with him to Mount Tabor to celebrate the Feast of Tabernacles. "We will celebrate the way our ancestors did," he told us, "in the wilderness."

It was late afternoon when we came to the place Jesus had chosen for us to camp. We set about erecting the canopy while John collected wood for the fire. We had brought lamb strips, onions, turnips, and eggplant to roast, and goat cheese and four loaves of bread. Miriam had sent along sweet fennel cakes, and Peter had brought a skin of wine. It was a proper meal for the feast.

Blessing the food, Jesus said, "Let us eat with gratitude to the Holy One. It will be our last meal for a while. After this our nourishment will come from God alone." After we ate, we joined hands and danced around the fire and sang the songs of our youth until the night grew cold. Then we wrapped ourselves in our cloaks and drew close to the fire. Jesus and I told stories of our boyhood to Peter and to John, who was too young to know of the mischief the older cousins got into whenever we were together. We bedded down in the glow of friendship and wine.

When I woke the next morning, I saw Jesus sitting still as a rock with his face to the East. His eyes were closed, and his lips were moving. I slowed my breath and was able to hear his chant: "I am in Thee, Thou art in my body, Holy One. Spirit of God, we are one."

I thought about Moses, who had come to a mount like this, who had seen the face of God and lived. I wondered if the oneness that Jesus seemed to be experiencing was like that which Moses felt when he stepped on holy ground. I wanted to feel this same oneness, but I knew I was not worthy. I felt a dark mood come over me even as the light of the morning sun came upon us. I pulled my cloak over my head. "What is it you want me to do?" I prayed to the God I could not see or feel. "Have I not obeyed your commandments? Have I not given up even my livelihood to serve you?" Suddenly tears like those of a child formed in my eyes.

I felt Jesus' hand on my shoulder, and I looked up at him, now sitting before me with the sun behind him. "What is it that is distressing you, cousin?" he asked.

"I have given God all I have." I was weeping now. "But he rejects my offering just as he did Cain's."

He pressed me. "And why do you think he rejected Cain's offering?"

"I could never understand this," I told him. "Cain gave God the first fruits of his labor! To this day, our tradition tells us to give the first fruits. But he refused Cain's offering."

Jesus said, "Do you remember the words that God spoke to Cain?" Of course, I could not. "His words were, 'Sin is crouching at your door and wants to rule you.' What

God wanted from Cain was for him to face the truth of the evil that was in his heart."

"What evil was that?" I asked.

"His hatred for Abel, his brother. God wanted a pure heart. This is what he wants from you."

"But Cain killed his brother!" I protested. "My brother sleeps unmolested under the canopy!"

"Remember, James, what I told you. What is bound on Earth is bound in Heaven. John's body is there unharmed, but his spirit has been whipped and crushed since he was a small boy."

I was stunned. I looked at my brother, tangled in his cloak, his frame slim like our mother's. "I have always seen him as weak like a woman." I could not believe the words that were pouring out from my mouth.

"Your father, Zebedee, punished John for his weakness and celebrated your strength," Jesus said. "Your mother, Salome, tried to protect John the way a mother bird protects her chick."

"In my eyes, she loved him more," I said. This was a moment of truth for me, and I felt briefly a burden slip from my shoulders.

"And so you drew close to your father and did what pleased him, which was to see the stronger of his two boys emulate him in abusing the brother that he, too, considered weak."

I opened my mouth to defend my father and myself, but no words came. I knew Jesus was speaking the truth. "So my sacrifice is worthless, just as it was for Cain."

"Yes, because it is not the sacrifice the Holy One asks from you. What the Holy One requires is your heart, James."

"My heart is broken," I told him. "I have sinned against God and against my brother."

Then he said, his voice soft, "In the Kingdom of God, what is broken is made whole again. Anger is turned into love. Sadness is turned into joy. You need only open your eyes and see and with your ears listen."

"I am not worthy to do this work, Jesus." I told him. "After this retreat I will return to Capernaum and to my father's boat."

"You are worthier than ever," he said. "There is only one thing you have yet to do, the one thing Cain could not."

"What is that?" I asked.

"Look there. John is waking from his sleep. Remember how I said what is loosed on Earth is loosed in Heaven? Go to your brother. Speak your new words, words that flow from your love, not from your contempt. He will be healed, and you will be healed as well."

I did as Jesus asked. John and I were born brothers in the flesh, but that day we were born as brothers in the Spirit.

I miss Jesus, but in relating this story of what he saw and did to heal my soul, I can feel his presence once again.

My heart is heavy for Mary, his mother and our aunt, for his brothers and sisters, and for Miriam. Thank you, Yakov, for leading us in this time to remember.

YAKOV

Our family used to call James *Ben Ra'am*, which means "son of thunder," but he no longer bears that name. What a transformation! But then, not one of us comes into the Kingdom without being changed. One could call the gate *change*. This is true for me, for James, and for our next speaker, Andrew.

Andrew said to me one time, "There is no depth to which Jesus will not go to root out that which keeps a person from entering the Kingdom of God."

Andrew, as James said, was in the boat that day when Yeshua first revealed his mission. Please come forward, dear friend. Tell us what your memory is of that day and of the days that followed.

ANDREW

Yes, that was a day when the lives of four fishermen were changed.

As James already told you, I blamed the Baptist for bringing the wrath of Herod upon himself. Those who know me will tell you my philosophy is to walk softly when lions are prowling—just say your prayers humbly and don't draw attention to yourself. That is what I believed, but it was not the way for the Baptist. When he saw signs of sin he spoke out boldly, even against those who had the power over life and death.

My brother Peter and I are originally from Bethsaida, but we grew up in Capernaum. When we were men we became fishermen and later joined Zebedee and his sons. Peter and I first heard about the Baptist from a man who came looking for work when the fish were running strong. He told us the Baptist was known to preach at Hajlah Ford north of where the river empties into the Dead Sea. The two of us went down there to see for ourselves. I was impressed by the Baptist's choice to rid himself of all earthly possessions, so unlike the religious leaders I had seen in the Temple. More important was his message of repentance. "Change your ways to be in accordance with God's will for you," he preached. He spoke about the poor and being fair and just in one's work. Both Peter and I chose to go into the river to be baptized, and back home we talked to others about his message.

Peter and I first met Jesus there at Hajlah and were surprised when one day he showed up in Capernaum. This is when we learned about his relationship with Zebedee and his family.

I was more than willing to respond to the challenge Jesus set before us that day in the boat. You might say I was one of those sheep who had lost his shepherd when the Baptist died.

In those early days before we left Capernaum, life in the community was so simple and joyous, was it not? Often we gathered in Peter's house and listened to Jesus' message about this Kingdom of his. On warm days we would go down to the shore of the lake, where townspeople would come to hear him. If the people were hungry, Perpetua, her mother Eunice, Salome, and Arsinoe would come down the hill with baskets of bread.

Can you remember the dance Jesus did when he talked about the Kingdom? He would reach up to the sky as though he were plucking pears from a tree. Then he would hold the imaginary fruit in his arms and pretend to pass them to the people. He did this with great animation, biting the fruit and licking his beard as he went about. "Taste and eat," he said. "This is the Kingdom of God. Open your eyes and you will see," he said. "When the hungry are fed, *that* is the Kingdom of God. When you see those who grieve being comforted, you are looking at the Kingdom of God.

"When you enter the Kingdom," he said, "you will be surprised. From then on, when you are persecuted, you will not want to retaliate. Rather, you will respond to your enemy with forgiveness, for *this* is how the Kingdom lives within you. If you see evil in your friend, you will not cast him into darkness but rather bring him into the light. Even when you see that the evil is inside your own self, the Spirit will come in and sweep away those spirits until your floors are clean."

Whenever Jesus spoke, it felt like my cup was running over. I can understand how it is that the people found themselves full of hope, for he awakened them to what love can do.

I remember one cold night when a crowd gathered in Peter's house to listen to Jesus preach. There were so many that we were packed between the walls like pickles in a barrel. Suddenly chunks of mud began to fall on Jesus' head. We looked up to see that someone was tearing back the tiles on the roof. Jesus stopped speaking and looked up to see a man being lowered down in a sling supported by ropes. "What is this?" Jesus shouted to the men managing the ropes.

"This man is dying, Jesus of Nazareth," one of them shouted. "We brought him here so you might heal him."

We worked together to get the man to the floor and laid him out. We could see the man was barely breathing, nothing but an anxious rattle. His lips were white and dry, and he was mumbling. Jesus knelt down beside him and put his ear to his mouth and listened to his weak words. Jesus said, "Yes," and listened more. "Yes," Jesus said again. He did this several times while he caressed the man's head, as though wiping away his fever. Then he stood and took the man by the hand and helped him get to his feet. Everyone cheered and praised God to see the man stand on his own. Jesus looked up through the open hole in the roof at the men and said, "See what love can do! With no thought of self, these men did all they could for their friend. You see above you the faces of the Kingdom of God."

I cannot understand how it is that Jesus suffered the same fate as the Baptist. (Please forgive me for my tears.) What is it about him or about John that enraged religious leaders so much that they would want them to die? I asked

Joanna one day if her husband, Chuza, who worked for Herod, had words to say about this matter. She said Chuza told her that when people hear and understand Jesus' message, they stop listening to the religious leaders. The leaders have always been known as the bearers of the truth. This is a place of privilege and honor, she said, but more important, of power.

I understood then it was because of jealousy that Jesus was taken from us. But Joanna comforted me, saying, "They took his body, but his Spirit remains." I know she is right because of the love we have for one another as we gather here today. Look around, brothers and sisters, and see the Kingdom of God.

YAKOV

Andrew, you were not alone in your thoughts about John who came to be called the Baptist. He was, as you know, a member of our own family. In breaking away from the Temple, he brought heartache to his mother, Elizabeth, and shame to his father, Zechariah, himself a priest.

I, too, judged John, but I know now my judgment was unfair. As a priest myself, I clung to the Temple practice: the symbols of water and sacrifices and fire and oil, the reading of the Torah and the singing of psalms—these define my soul. For my cousin John to turn his back on all of this was scandalous to me and an embarrassment.

But you are right, Andrew, in what you say today. John's was a simple message of repentance: turn away from one way of life to another, from selfishness to justice and charity. How can this be contrary to what the Creator wants?

As for John's manner of living, he is not to be criticized. Had I thought it through, the child Yochana, as we called him, was forever wandering into the woods to catch bugs or commune with the rock badger. The birds flocked to him, and the lizards shared the sunlight with him. In leaving to join the community of the wilderness he was only following the dictates of his own soul. Isn't this what is expected of each of us?

Jesus called not just men to follow him, but women as well. It was so contrary to our ways, and yet he saw the divine in a woman as much as in a man. He once said to me, "To reject women is to look at God with one eye covered." You will be hearing from all the seven women who served, but first I introduce you to Suzanna, who comes from Magdala. Tell us, dear woman, what is it that Jesus gave to you that you would like to pass on to all of us?

SUZANNA

I am honored to be the first woman to speak here today, even though I was the last of the women to follow him. Dear sisters, we remember a Jesus the men do not. Always intruding, with that mischievous smile and light in his eyes, he insisted we are far more interesting than the men.

"The Kingdom of God is made of those who serve, not those who dine," he said to us. "You need to teach the men."

Jesus also said, "In the Kingdom of God there is neither male nor female, only souls who find joy in serving others. So no one remains naked without a cloak and no one dies alone." And he told us where the Kingdom is: "It is here now, as we cut vegetables and feed the hungry." Then he would take up a knife and begin chopping.

Mary, you understood that your son was chosen even before he was born. You worked his heart like a woman kneading dough. You showed him his strength, yet you insisted that he respect his sisters. It took a long time for the yeast to raise the bread, and now here we are, seven women talking about Jesus as though he were our brother, just as he was to the men.

I first heard Jesus' message when he came to preach on the shore of Lake Galilee, not far from Magdala. I knew of his coming because of the arrangement of the leaves in my cup. I prayed, and the spirits said to me, "Go!"

So I went to hear him, but I sat behind the old sycamore that local people call Sarah's Weaving so that no one would notice me. The women of Magdala hated me, and their men dared not admit they knew me. I will never forget the words Jesus spoke that seemed meant for me alone: "God's kingdom is for those who are spiritually poor." Those few words ignited in me a hope that God might love even this sinful woman.

Later, I went to Chuza's home near Tiberius, where I heard that Jesus had gone. When I got to the door, his wife, Joanna, met me. She took me into her arms like a mother holds a grieving child. "I know Jesus will want to see you," she said.

There he was in Chuza's parlor, sitting in a circle with men of importance. They all knew who I was. One knew me intimately. That one glared at me with his harsh judgment, telling me with dark eyes hidden beneath his bushy brows I had no right to be there, not because I was a woman, for Joanna was there, but because I was a sinner. I was not deterred because I knew his guilt was as great as mine.

At first I just huddled near the door. I could see Jesus noticed me, but he kept right on talking. "My Kingdom is not of this world," he was saying. "One who is in it sees things others do not, for those of this world perceive with their senses using only their eyes and ears. Thus, the only kingdom they can imagine is one they see and hear and feel with their touch. But I tell you the physical world is only a reflection of the Kingdom about which I speak. It is like looking into still waters. One can see the tree in the water, but the reflection is not the real tree. Those who have opened their inner eye know what I am talking about. They understand what others cannot. Joanna is one of those who sees the world differently. What the world deems broken, the Spirit sees as whole. What the world condemns, the Spirit loves. See how she welcomed this woman. Joanna is Sophia. She wears the face of the living God."

"Come to me, Suzanna," Jesus said, holding his hand out toward me. I could not believe he knew my name. "You are carrying a heavy burden, and God wants to take it from you." I gave him my hand, and he led me to sit before him. As I did, I prostrated myself. I could not look at him because of my tears. They dripped on his feet, and I tried to wipe them with my hair.

"Do you know who this woman is?" It was the man who had condemned me with his gaze.

Jesus looked at him and said, "Perhaps you would like to throw the first stone!" The man, stunned by Jesus' rebuke, rose up and stalked out of Chuza's house.

"What God has repaired," Jesus said to all who remained, "no man can tear apart."

"Amen," said Chuza. The others said the same. I knew I was home.

Then Jesus spoke words that made me wonder how it is that he knew me so well. "You are a child of God," he said. "Because of your work with spirits you have been able to see them when others cannot. But the Spirit of God has taken up residence in you now. You will continue to see spirits, for this is a gift, but now you will be able to discern the evil ones and drive them out. Be glad, for great is the reward for you in Heaven. The suffering you have endured is not different than that of the prophets before you. It was out of their own darkness that they came to know the light. Remember your days of darkness this way—as a path to the light."

So I became one among you. Jesus often let me come with him where spirits were seeking to seize control. Together we would lay hands upon those who were tormented, he the men and I the women. Together we prayed, and always the spirits dispersed as they had for me the day he welcomed me into the Kingdom.

My friends, nothing is lost. Every pain, every rejection, every fear is transformed. What once tormented me became my gift to others. What was darkness became light. Even death is transformed. Jesus lives! He speaks in and through us. I pray all of you will come to see what the Spirit has shown me.

YAKOV

I am deeply humbled, Suzanna. My brother tried many times to get me to see what you were able to grasp so readily. My heart aches knowing I let him go to his death without seeing me awaken.

Now I would like Simon to come and speak.

I met Simon the first time I served in the Temple. The younger priests used to sit with students to discuss different aspects of the Torah.

How surprised I was when, years later, I saw that Jesus had chosen this zealot to follow him. My brother had an ability, it seems, to look deeply, beyond religious and political differences.

I welcome you, Simon, and I am eager to hear your story.

SIMON

I cannot bear this. Jesus is dead, yet the tone of this gathering is much like a wedding. Are your hearts not as heavy as mine? You see light, but I see only darkness, thick and black like the inside of his tomb. I think of him lying there, alone on the cold stone slab, with no one to wash away the blood, no one to place herbs about him.

Dear brothers and sisters, I have a confession to make to you, for the lie is eating away at the wall of my heart. I cannot sleep. I have little appetite. In my mind I go over and over again the events before his death. I look back and see there were moments when I could have spoken out: when we first received word of the plot against him, at our last meal, at his arrest in the garden, when we stood huddled outside the house of Caiaphas. At each of these times I chose silence.

I have tried to explain away my actions, or lack of action, to convince myself that what I did was the right thing. But I keep losing the arguments with myself. I am neither a good lawyer nor a good judge. I am not even a good man. So I must speak. I cannot keep my secret any longer or I will surely die.

You see, I knew what Judas was doing. I knew, yet I did nothing to stop him. He had me convinced that if we turned Jesus over to the authorities, the people would rise up against Rome and at last claim the kingdom. But the plot failed . . . it failed.

I have had to face the truth that all along there were doubts in my mind. They were like persistent knocks at the door, but I refused to open it. Jesus said over and over again there were those who wanted to stop him. He even said, "One of these is in our midst." He said this at our last meal. We all looked at him in disbelief. Do you remember? Even Judas looked around in confusion, but that was for your sake, lest you suspect him. He had already betrayed Jesus. When Judas left, you all thought he was going to settle the cost for the meal, but I knew better. Again I said nothing. Oh, my God in Heaven! I knew!

Please believe me when I say I did not know the whole truth. Not until the very end. Even as they took him at Gethsemane, I thought the people would rise up—that they would have seen enough. But then, as they neared the place of the skull, I felt as though a vise was clamped around my chest. I knew it was over. Satan had won. And we, Judas and I, were his servants.

"Savior" we called him. Jesus did not like that claim. He rebuked us. But when we saw how the people loved him, we set our hopes so high we could no longer hear him. He would establish a new kingdom like David's. We heard his word that what is on Earth is in Heaven. This, we believed, meant he came from Heaven to build his kingdom on Earth. Our plans were only to hurry the inevitable.

Oh, dear God! I see now he was building the Kingdom every time he spoke, every time he touched, every time he ate with us, every time he held a child or a flower. When he walked through the fields and streets of a town, he carried the Kingdom with him. The Kingdom was in him. Wherever he went, there was the Kingdom. And when he loved, the Kingdom poured out of him like a living stream.

There is no more I can say. Dear friends . . . do I dare call you that? Please forgive me. Forgive me. Forgive me.

YAKOV

It is difficult for me to know what to say. My heart is not ready for this, Simon. It is not my place to condemn you, but I wonder how it is that a man can cooperate with evil in order to achieve something he deems to be right. How is this right? Is there no place for what it is that God wants, or is man to decide the fate of humanity?

Philip, perhaps you can bring me into the light.

PHILIP

Yakov, I can see the pain this new revelation brings to you and your family. I am sorry it comes to you today, when we gather to move out of the intense grief and darkness of sheloshim into another, gentler place where we can celebrate the good and happy moments with our beloved one.

I know you do not understand these things now, but believe me when I say light and darkness, life and death, and right and left are all siblings and inseparable. What this means is the Holy Spirit tends to everything and rules over all powers, whether tame or wild and running loose. In other words, even those who have gone astray are offspring of the Spirit. I cannot say how Judas fit into the divine plan, but surely he does. Perhaps one day we will understand how this is.

As for you, Simon, I praise God that your eyes have

been opened. You are in the light, though you cannot comprehend it. You heard James's story and how he felt when he first saw the truth about how he had wounded his brother. But see what James did! He went to his brother and confessed his sin. Once the inflictor of John's wounds, he became the healer. We have heard your confession and rejoice because our oneness is restored. Believe what I am saying to you. Look around and see love and compassion on the faces of your brothers and sisters.

What James has done, and now Simon as well, is what we must all do. It is our task to dig down deep to the evil within us and pull it out. It can only be uprooted if we recognize it. But if we are ignorant of it, it grows in us and produces fruit in our hearts. It dominates us. We are its slaves. It takes us captive so that we do what we do not want and we fail to do what we want. It is powerful because we do not recognize it. And for as long as it exists, it stays active.

For myself, the evil within was the great pride I had in my own righteousness. Nathaniel and I have been best friends since the time we were boys. You all know him to be a truly humble and authentic man, the exact opposite of what I was. Yet, even though he often pointed out my errors, I was not able to believe this awful truth about myself. I continued to stand firm in my judgment against those who were, in my eyes, not worthy to be among the chosen people of God.

One day, in exasperation, Jesus said to me, "Brother Philip, you are not God!" That was the moment of change for me. Were it not for Jesus' faith in me, I would still be living in my sinful mind.

Miriam, companion of Jesus, he loved you more than any of the disciples. If anyone wonders why this is so, I will tell you. Jesus himself had moments when he felt great darkness. At those times it was Miriam who led him out. The rest of us had expectations of him that were not his to fill. But because she and Jesus were of one spirit, she knew what he needed.

I have little more to say but to share with you a parable. There was once a householder who had everything: children, slaves, cattle, dogs, and pigs. The householder was wise and knew the food of each being. He fed the children baked bread and meat. He fed the slaves oil and grain. He fed the cattle barley, chaff, and fodder. He threw bones to the dogs. He fed the pigs acorns and gruel.

So it is with the disciples of God. Be wise. Do not be deceived by bodily forms, but examine the condition of each person's soul by speaking appropriately. Feed each exactly what their soul needs, just as the wise householder did. This is what our master did and what he wants us to do.

God bless you. Thank you all for being with us.

YAKOV

You are a true friend, Philip. The Spirit dwells in you just as it did in my brother, and the words you speak are the Father's words. In some way, my heart knows this to be true.

Jesus' body is gone from us, but he said, "Love one another as I have loved you." This means to me that we are to be to each member just as he was to us. So we humbly confess our sin, revealing to one another the truth of the darkness in us. And with the same humility we forgive as he did. We are all wounded healers. I see this truth now in the mercy and forgiveness that you, Philip, have shown Simon, and I am inspired to follow your lead.

What we need now is some joy. Of the many signs of the Spirit within, I am most fond of joy. There is one among us who fills my soul every time she comes into my presence. I am speaking of my own sister, Mara. Mara is a musician and dancer, and she attracts children like blossoms attract bees. Today she wishes to bring the children before us to lift up our hearts.

So come, little sister, and gift us with what you and the children have planned.

MARA

Jesus often said that when one part of the body is hurting, all parts share the pain because we are one. It is just as true that, because of our oneness, the healthy ones lift up those parts who are broken or lost. During this time of sheloshim, our family has been caught in a web like one woven by a spider, but you have come here to free us. This is what your words are doing for me, Philip, and I know for my mother and Yakov as well.

Yes, the children love to come because they understand what it means to be fully alive to joy. Jesus saw this and implored us to be like them, wide-eyed and full of wonder. Step into the Kingdom with me, dear family and friends.

My brother Jude will play the lyre for us. My brother Joses has the drums, and my sister Salome will play the tambourine. We gathered some sticks for the children to set the rhythm.

Let me introduce the children who are here to help us. Judah and Matya are my sister Salome's children. Petronilla is the daughter of Peter and Perpetua. She loves our little Simeon, but as you can see, she has trouble holding him, so my husband, Clopas, will help her. Joseph and Mariah are the children of my brother Joses.

We are going to sing a song that Jesus loved to sing. Many of you will remember it. Imagine him here with us now. "Come," he is saying. "Come all you children, even those with white hair and bad knees."

Joseph, Judah, and Mariah will do the actions that go with the song. Everyone, watch them and do as they do. The words are easy because we say them over and over again. Stand up, if you are able, and let your arms fly like happy birds.

Musicians, let's begin.

Come, little children, tell me what you know
about the ten secrets, seeds that help you grow.

We sing one, one, one . . .
One is our God in Heaven and on Earth.

Two, two, two . . .
Two are the tablets Moses brought down the hill.
One is our God in Heaven and on Earth.

Three, three, three . . .
Three for the fathers knowing what to do.
Two are the tablets Moses brought down the hill.
One is our God in Heaven and on Earth.

"What comes next, Matya? How many fingers? Four, yes four. Good for you! Your older brother has taught you well."

Four, four, four . . .
Four for the mothers seeing with their hearts.
Three for the fathers knowing what to do.
Two are the tablets Moses brought down the hill.
One is our God in Heaven and on Earth.

Five, five, five . . .
Five books of Torah guiding us to life.
Four for the mothers seeing with their hearts.
Three for the fathers knowing what to do.
Two are the tablets Moses brought down the hill.
One is our God in Heaven and on Earth.
Come little children; tell me what you know.
about the ten secrets, seeds to help you grow.

We sing six, six, six . . .
Six for the myrrh making Esther strong.
Five books of Torah guiding us to life.
Four for the mothers seeing with their hearts.
Three for the fathers knowing what to do.
Two are the tablets Moses brought down the hill.
One is our God in Heaven and on Earth.

Seven, seven, seven . . .
Seven days a week to love and to praise.
Six for the myrrh making Esther strong.
Five books of Torah guiding us to life.
Four for the mothers seeing with the heart.
Three for the Fathers knowing what to do.
Two are the tablets Moses brought down the hill.
One is our God in Heaven and on Earth.

Eight, eight, eight . . .
Eight is Josiah serving God on high.
Seven days a week to love and to praise.
Six for the myrrh making Esther strong.
Five books of Torah guiding us to life.
Four for the mothers seeing with their hearts.
Three for the fathers knowing what to do.
Two are the tablets Moses brought down the hill.
One is our God in Heaven and on Earth.

Nine, nine, nine . . .
Nine months to birth; a mother loves her child.
Eight is Josiah serving God on high.
Seven days a week to love and to praise.
Six for the myrrh making Esther strong.
Five books of Torah guiding us to life.
Four for the mothers seeing with their hearts.
Three for the fathers knowing what to do.
Two are the tablets Moses brought down the hill.
One is our God in Heaven and on Earth.

Ten, ten, ten . . .
Ten happy children dancing in the fields.
Nine months to birth; a mother loves her child.
Eight is Josiah serving God on high.
Seven days a week to love and to praise.
Six for the myrrh making Esther strong.
Five books of Torah guiding us to life.
Four for the mothers seeing with their hearts.
Three for the fathers knowing what to do.
Two are the tablets Moses brought down the hill.
One is our God in Heaven and on Earth.

See, little children, all that you know
about the ten secrets, seeds to help you grow.
Together let us plant them and watch them as they green,
bringing forth blossoms with more seeds to sow.

What better way to give praise to our God than to sing and dance together!

Thank you, children, for helping us to remember this song and for leading us. Even old Uncle Zebedee joined us in our dance—I could see his head bobbing and his fringes shaking. I bet he hasn't danced since his wedding. Am I right, Aunt Salome?

Clopas, do you remember our wedding dance? Jesus brought his new friends with him, and we met Andrew, Simon, and Judas for the first time. Peter and Matthew were there with their wives, Perpetua and Arsinoe. That was the beginning of this wonderful tapestry of women. These two women taught me how to be a wise wife and mother. They were there when I gave birth to Simeon. I could not have had better midwives than these. I think it is because of the labor of childbirth that we can speak of things like darkness and light, of brokenness and healing, of death into life.

What a joyful day when Clopas and I became one. So much joy, in fact, that we ran out of wine. Do you remember? Some blamed Jesus for bringing the extra guests, but some of us think Jude was in the jugs. We don't know this for sure, though. (Oh, Jude, you know I am teasing you).

There is nothing Jesus loved more than to gather with friends and family. He loved the food and drink and was the first to dance as soon as the musicians brought out their instruments. I can close my eyes and see him now.

In truth, dear friends, after this dark month of she-loshim, I was not sure whether there would be a song in me, but look what these children have done! Thank you, little ones, and thank you all who joined us in the song.

YAKOV

Mara and children, you have inspired me to sing a song of praise, one first sung by David when he was full of gratitude to his Lord and King.

I pray to you, O Lord,
you hear my voice in the morning,
at sunrise I offer my prayer . . .
and wait upon you to answer.

You are not a God who is pleased with wrongdoing.
You allow no evil in your presence.
You cannot stand the sight of pride.
You hate all wickedness.
You are a destroyer of lies, violence, and deceit.

Because of your love
I can come into your house;
I can worship in your Holy Temple,
I can bow down in reverence,
I can rise up to dance and shout out in joy.

All who find safety in you will rejoice.
They always sing for joy
Because of you they are happy.

It is not a good thing to hold back the Spirit that is in us. This is the lesson I have learned from the children today. Thank you, Mara, for this great gift.

My brother Jude will speak now. He has already blessed us with the lyre; now he blesses us again with his story. It is a story of redemption. You will see.

JUDE

Thank you for leading us in song, Mara. As sad as we are, we need to remember that Jesus wanted us to play. This is a characteristic of the Kingdom, and if we fail to play, the Kingdom will soon be empty.

We are here to mourn my brother's death, but we all must face the same, for dying is part of living here in the earthly kingdom. I for my part have already known death, a spiritual death, but now I stand before you very much alive.

Simon, I understand what it is to have regrets. Judas was your best friend, and it is understandable that you did not want to betray him. In the end it was Jesus who was betrayed, but how could you know this? I wish Judas had known of your love for him. Love can save. It saved me.

Mara, Clopas, I am not the one responsible for the jugs going dry at your wedding, but I could have been. I had more than my share that night. I always had more than my share. I thought the proverbs that laud the wonders of wine and the joy it brings were written especially for me. But eventually the joy was replaced by misery. What started out as my friend turned into my enemy. Instead of me having a share of wine, wine had its share of me.

What grief I brought to my mother! She told me once that my father cannot rest easy in his grave because of me. My father, Joseph . . . such a righteous man he was! I remember one day when Jesus was making a small house with scraps from the woodbin, and I was mocking him. To get me to go away, he shoved me. It was not a brutal shove, just a tap on the shoulder with his hammer. Rascal that I was, I went crying to Father, holding my shoulder as though it were broken. He went to Jesus, grabbed his hammer, and smashed the little house, shouting, "This is what you do to your brothers and sisters when you hurt them! We are here to build up, not to tear down!" I never told my brother how sorry I was for what I had done.

It was not just Jesus I betrayed. I betrayed everyone in my family at one time or another. After I became free at last, I prayed for my God to show me ways to rebuild what I had destroyed. As I joined in the work, Jesus showed me many ways to do this. He understood I needed to believe in my own goodness. "See the gift that you are," he said to me.

Simon, this is what I pray for you: that you will see the

gift that you are. In sharing your truth, you reveal to us our own selves. We need to do this for one another.

There was a story my brother used to tell. I know you will all remember it because he told it often. It was a story about a young man with a rebellious nature who wanted to go off on his own rather than stay home to help with the family business. He demanded that his father give him his inheritance, even though he was still young. His father's heart was broken, but he did as his son requested. The boy went out and lived a life not unlike the one I lived. His father waited mournfully for him to return home. I know I caused my family to suffer as well. The proverbs tell us wine robs us of our senses. This was true for me. I had no sense of the pain I caused.

Yakov, you played an important role in my facing the truth. One day you grabbed me as I was storming out of the house. You said, "Listen to me! You are full of anger, and because of this you will never achieve what the Creator intends for you. Get rid of your filthy habit and evil conduct. You are like a man who looks in a mirror and sees himself, but immediately turns away and forgets what he saw. You tell me you are sick and tired of this so-called life of yours, and then you turn away and forget what you said as soon as your friends come around again."

After Jesus came back from the East, he took me aside. I expected the same thrashing as the one I'd gotten from

Yakov. But, instead, he spoke about himself. "John sent me into the wilderness," he said. "He told me there God would show me what he wanted me to do with my life. So I went with great expectations. But when I was there, I could not hear the voice of God. Day after day, I prayed and fasted and wept until I was as dry as a bone. I had dreams that were so frightening I would curl up in a ball and shake. I had gone there full of power, but I felt I was being squeezed like a wineskin that was totally empty.

"It was in this dry place," Jesus said, "that God showed me how bereft I was. There is no power but God's. All other power comes from the false self and leads to nothingness." Then he said to me, "Jude, you don't have the power to free yourself from this bondage. Only God has the power."

I heard my brother's words, but I did not know how to access this power. I went down to the lake. The night was cloudy, so I sat in total darkness. I never felt so alone in my life. Finally, a slight breeze swept across the surface of the water and the dome of the sky opened. I looked up and saw a million lights above me. Suddenly I knew I was not alone. I began to cry, but now I was not crying over my poor self. I cried tears of wonderment at the mercy of God.

I drank no wine after that. It was difficult for only a short time because Jesus and his friends gathered me in. They were like the stars that guide sailors adrift in the night.

As you go out to bring others into the Kingdom, you

will find people who are always grumbling and blaming others. They follow their own desires. They brag about themselves and flatter others in order to have their own way. They never follow through on their promises. Remember what God has done for me, one of your own brothers in the Lord. He saw a precious stone in a pile of dung and pulled it out. Show these people mercy. Forgive them as God has forgiven you. It is only through love that you will be able to save them. Nothing . . . nothing . . . works but love.

If someone already among us falls, keep inviting them back into the fold, for didn't Jesus tell us about the good shepherd who left the ninety-nine to seek out the one that was lost?

Today, I believe I am becoming the human being the Father created me to be. I thank all of you for this. I miss my brother terribly, yet he gave me so much that I can spend the rest of my days pondering these things. Thank you all for being here. Your presence means so much to me and my family.

YAKOV

I regret that our father, Joseph, did not remain on this earth to see you come home, Jude. He loved you with as much love as the Holy One. But these thoughts can only deepen our regret. We need to dwell on what we have gained.

Now my young cousin John, brother of James, from whom you heard earlier, would like to speak. After my brother's death, he took our mother into his home in Capernaum so she could be near her sister Salome during the month of sheloshim. She told me John was a great comfort to her, seeing to the duties she found impossible to do in her grief.

In a similar way, I am told John was always at Jesus' right hand, attending to the smallest tasks necessary to accomplish all the good works. As a priest, I know it is this attention to detail that holds a temple together.

Come, John, and share with us. We are in need of comfort.

JOHN

What James and Andrew told you about that day on Lake Galilee is exactly how it was. I could not believe Jesus wanted me to come with him. What did I have to offer? I was the boy who buried the guts of the fish, not a fisher of men. But I was so taken by him! He was for me what my earthly father was not. Every good work I did, Jesus saw. Every insight I shared he received as though from a scholar. Every good quality I had buried, he drew forth. Serving him was what I desired. He was my light.

"John," he said to me, "I am not the father that you seek. The one you seek is above all, the Eternal God, the Source of Life. He is your true Father. You see him in me because I obey him. The words I speak are not my own but his." This was the message to me on Mount Tabor. For the rest of the time I worked with him, I struggled with this. But now, the Father himself has spoken to me.

After Jesus' death, I went up to the Temple to pray. A Pharisee named Arimanias approached me and said, "Where is your teacher whom you followed?"

I thought to myself, *How is it that this man standing before me did not even know of Jesus' death?* What felt to me like the earth shifting was nothing to him.

Then he said, "The Nazarene really has deceived you, filled your ears with lies, closed your mind, and turned you from the traditions of your ancestors."

When I heard this, I ran from the Temple and went to Gethsemane, at the Mount of Olives, where Jesus had prayed before the arrest. My heart was rent, and I cried out, "Why did you send him here only to come to this end?" As I was thinking these thoughts, the heavens opened and the sky lit up. I saw an elderly person standing near, and he said, "John, John, why are you doubting? Why are you afraid? I am the Father, and I will always be with you." That is when I knew what the Beloved had told me was true. The Father he proclaimed is my own.

I want to tell you about the last days. Many of you have not heard this. Because Caiaphas's servant knew me as the one who delivered my father's fish, I was allowed into the jail when Jesus was taken there after his arrest. I watched as he attempted to defend himself before the Sanhedrin. I could not believe how each truth Jesus spoke was twisted and reconstructed to convict him. I sat with him late into the night, long after the interrogation was over. He was full of despair. "I don't want to die," he said. "It is difficult for me to accept this cup." Then he added, perhaps for me, "But the darkness cannot comprehend the light. They don't know what they are doing."

And so it was. The events unfolded as they did because the darkness was in control. But, my brothers and sisters, Jesus was not conquered even by death! Did he not say to us when we ate together for the last time that he would be with us? I don't know that he ever spoke with such passion as he did that night. "This is why I came," he said, "to show you the Father's love." He knew what was to come, for he said, "In a little while I will not be with you, but do not be discouraged or afraid, because the Spirit that dwells in me dwells in you also. You will be able to do everything and anything I have done." We have to believe this if we are to continue the work he started.

I want to say something to Simon. I was sitting next to Jesus at the table that night. He himself knew what Judas was doing, yet he did not stop him. Why do you berate yourself for failing to do what Jesus himself chose not to do? Jesus knew what was in the minds and hearts of the leaders, and he also knew they would have their way with or without Judas's participation. Sometimes the movement of events around us evades our control, and our only choice is to let go and trust that the Father's purpose is never thwarted. We need to remember the events that most threaten us are of the earthly kingdom. "Be not afraid," Jesus said of them.

To my cousin Jude, I have only this: Jesus told me he would have stayed in the East, but the Father told him to go back to the lost children of Israel. Upon his return to his homeland, he saw that his own brother, whom he left as an innocent child and whom he loved, was one of the lost ones. But you turned around, and watching you grow was his delight. You have shown us by your life the full measure of the Father's compassion.

Dear friends, do you see how it is? First, there is the Father's love. Jesus taught us that we all, through Christ, are one with the Father. All is love, Father, sons and daughters, and the Spirit that moves us. We have seen it here today in the revelations and in forgiveness and compassion offered. We have reached down into the darkness of despair and lifted one another up into the light.

May the Spirit dwell in us and through us as we continue to gather the lost ones into the Kingdom of God.

YAKOV

Heavy on my heart are the many students who used to come to the Temple with their anxious questions about the Torah and the will of God. Most of them still had their woman voices, and they greeted us priests with their little salaam and their mouths hanging open as we fleshed out the law's many facets.

To be sure, such intense inquiry boosted my priestly ego, but at the same time I found their innocence draining. It felt to me like offering a man coming out of the desert one thimbleful of water. I used to ruminate for days on words I wished I had spoken to some sad, confused boy who left just as thirsty for God as when he came.

I never stopped to ask myself why my answers were so unsatisfying to a searching soul. Jesus knew, and he tried to tell me. He had gone himself to the Temple as a boy, he reminded me, and he always left unsatisfied. "A priest does not have the answers because he sits in the Temple," he said. "Before God there are not priests, only empty hearts waiting to be filled."

John, thank you for your profound message. It is the one these young men needed to hear about the one Father who loves us all.

You have already heard from James and now from his brother John. You saw their father Zebedee shake his fringes when he rose to dance with the children. Salome is the mother of this thunderous brood. Please, dear lady, share with us your insights.

SALOME

Thank you, Yakov. You are doing a fine job. And our Creator is doing a fine job, as well, by providing us with sun and warmth for this day of remembering.

But the days before this have not been so fine. Women who have been in labor know the pain that comes in bringing a life into the world. Women know, too, the pain that accompanies letting life go out from the world. It is women's work to prepare the body after death; it is women's work to wail with the bereaved during the deep darkness of loss. This was the work of our mothers and their mothers before them.

Yet, how great is this tradition of sheloshim, for we do not have to face the darkness alone. And how great is this ritual in which we accompany the bereaved out of the darkness. There will be more days of mourning, and the women will continue to be there, but for now we must stop to let in the light. As difficult as it is, we must try to remember the good days once again.

Mary, dear sister, you lived to see your son do the work of his Father in Heaven, the work he was created to do. Is this not the yearning of every Jewish mother? For this to happen, mothers sometimes have to let go of their own dreams. I have had to do this for my two boys.

I would like to share my fondest memory of Jesus. I am a baker. He told me, "My dear Aunt Salome, you can make a loaf of bread the way no other man or woman can." He said this to me only one time and then, after that, whenever he broke off a piece of my loaf and bit into it, he would look up into the sky and then at me and then back at the sky again, all the while smiling as he chewed. It was like a secret sign he had for me. It made me burst with pride.

Jesus liked to use bread to teach about the Kingdom of God. When the disciples would come back discouraged after going into the villages, he would say, "Kneading is hard work." When the baskets of bread were passed among the families who sat in the fields to hear him, he would take one of my long loaves and say, "Take and eat! Just as our bodies take in the food of the earth, the Holy Spirit moves in and through us, causing us to grow in love for God and one another." He did this again at our last meal together.

I understood and I remember because I am a baker, but Jesus spoke to everyone in a way that let them comprehend the Kingdom. To the farmer he spoke of seeds and soil, planting and harvesting. To the moneylender he spoke of investing and profits and losses. To the potter or the tinker he talked about vessels of clay or metal. The shepherd understood his message about the sheep that know the shepherd's voice and the wolf that waits for the shepherd to sleep. There was nothing Jesus could not use to teach. For him, all things of the earth were tools to teach about the Kingdom of God. To someone struggling to understand, he would say, "Consider this . . . or that . . . a jewel, a rock, an oil lamp, a fisherman's net, a well, a sickle . . . or a child." Yes, a child. Even a child is a window into the Kingdom of God.

How Jesus loved the children! Peter and Perpetua, my heart swells in my breast when I recall your little Petronilla reaching out to Jesus. I recall the day he first came into your home, and there she was, sitting in her sling chair in the corner of your kitchen. He spoke to her softly, then gently scooped her up into his arms. We were accustomed to seeing Petronilla stiff, with her little hands turned in. But as soon as Jesus held her, she relaxed and sighed. No one dared question his touch. We all knew, no matter what the law says, that Jesus saw her as the purest lamb in God's eyes. She was his favorite, but he never turned away any of the children. He told us they are our teachers. "They can see the Kingdom," he said. "Let them show you the way."

Thank you all for being here, dear friends. You have said, Miriam, "Love begets love." We must remember this always. It is the yeast in the dough, and we must work it together so the bread will rise.

YAKOV

I want to thank my aunt for speaking of this important work of women to accompany us into and then out of life. Salome has fulfilled her role with grace and love, holding our mother and our whole family this past month of mourning. She stayed faithfully with the task, and now she invites us to celebrate his life.

I invite you to enjoy Salome's bread as we pass baskets among you. There are also fennel cakes and sugared rinds. Please take these and enjoy the sweetness of this time we have together.

Our next speaker is Joanna. Chuza and Joanna are old friends of our family. Their home near Magdala was a stopping place for Jesus when he traveled between Judea and Capernaum. When he visited, it often happened that men of importance gathered to listen to him. Employed by Herod, Chuza was an asset to the movement because of his political connections. Joanna has considerable knowledge of the Galilean terrain and a gift of healing.

Come tell us, Joanna, what are your memories of Jesus?

JOANNA

I suppose I am the only one among you whom Jesus did not choose to follow him. Rather, it was I who chose him. I saw what he could do for women such as Suzanna. I watched him heal the man mad with spirits who lived among the tombs. I saw him touch the untouchables without fear or shame. I myself was healed from the pain in my knees and was able to walk again, just as I had as a young woman.

"Let me come with you," I said to him. "I know the edible plants and healing herbs on the prairies and in the forests all over Galilee. I can be a great help to you."

Jesus looked across the table at my husband. Chuza was smiling. "Take her, Jesus," he said. "If I don't let her go, I will have to listen to her complain every day."

Thank you, Yakov, for your support of the service that Chuza provided for the movement. Because he was the chief steward in Herod's house, we learned the details of the Baptist's death, how while drunk and lustful, Herod ordered John's beheading. We know Herod Antipas is a corrupt man, weak of character and violent by nature.

When Chuza heard what Jesus said about the Temple leaders, he warned, "That is very dangerous. The leaders will not stand for it, especially if the number of followers keeps growing." We now know his words were prophetic. Chuza was exactly where God wanted him to be.

I know my joining the movement was difficult for some of you. Peter, you said it is not right that a woman should come without her husband. That is indeed what the law teaches. But Jesus disregarded this law as he did many others. To him, men and women are the same in that the Spirit of God dwells in each equally.

I don't intend to diminish the brothers, but to be a woman in the Kingdom is true glory. Jesus stood at the door and welcomed us because we are precious to the Father. I see what he did for so many women as we traveled. Suzanna of Magdala, the prophetess, has already spoken to you, and we are grateful for her beautiful story. The Samaritan woman is here with her family. We heard how Photini worked to spread the word about the Kingdom among her people. Veronica has come down from Capernaum. We all knew of your suffering and shame, and yet you went to him and he healed you. Praise God! And our dear Miriam, our leader. I can't wait to hear your words of wisdom.

I loved Jesus with my whole heart. To have even a small part in building the Kingdom has given my life meaning. Once I became part of the movement, I found myself waking up each day wondering what thing God would ask of me. There was always something, some act of service, a poor child to feed, an ailing grandfather to give ear to, an infection to salve and wrap.

There is goodness in each of you, and Jesus wanted us to see this. "Look!" he would say. "See the goodness in this heart. See the compassion in this soul." And we would look and think, "Yes! He is right!"

Let us continue to see what he saw. Let us continue to forgive, to heal, to play, and to love. Gracious is our God!

YAKOV

I know, Joanna, that you were an essential part of the mission as the community traveled around Galilee. Jesus spoke often of your work, as did the other disciples. It was common knowledge that if one need a healing salve or an herb to ease pain, Joanna could prepare it. Thank you for the good work you have done for this community.

Now I would like to invite Peter to come up. As one of the first to be chosen, he has been eager to speak his message about the Kingdom.

PETER

Those of you from Capernaum know it was in my home that the movement actually began, for it was there Jesus settled after returning from the East. There he gathered his first disciples, and we sat around Perpetua's table, learning about the Kingdom of God and then planning with him how to deliver his message to the people of Israel.

I recall vividly the day Matthew came. I would not have imagined Jesus choosing a tax collector as a disciple, but then again, Jesus did many things that surprised me. Matthew brought with him his beautiful wife, Arsinoe. Perpetua was delighted to have another woman come into the fold.

Of course my mother-in-law, Eunice, was there, too. I mention her because she was among the first to experience Jesus' healing touch when she was overcome with fever. True to her giving spirit, she rose immediately to continue to serve us.

My father, Jonah, is here today. As old as he is, he managed to come all the way from Bethsaida, which is where Andrew and I grew up. Joanna mentioned our little girl, Petronilla, whom you met when the children sang with Mara. Thank you, Mara, for doing that. Jesus loved the children, and he loved music and dance. It was a fitting and welcoming thing to do.

My support goes out to Jesus' family, especially his mother, Mary. There has never been a purer woman in all of Israel. You have suffered more these past weeks than anyone. If it is a consolation to you, know that Jesus' suffering was tempered by his knowing that what he had to go through served the Father's purpose.

Please, sister Joanna, I feel you have misunderstood me. My concern was not whether a woman comes with her husband, but whether she comes with his approval. This is the correct way to interpret the scripture. Clearly, Chuza gave you not only his approval, but also his blessing. After all, Chuza's needs are well attended in Herod's house. In addition, your children are now grown and self-sufficient. Don't you see? You were relieved of your duties and thus could come and serve the community. Praise God for working all things together.

Let me tell you more about the day in Zebedee's boat, when Jesus laid out his plan. We talked at length about the teachings of John the preacher. Andrew and I were the only ones who had been his followers, so we understood more than the others Jesus' anguish over the loss of his cousin. In their telling of the story, Andrew, James, and John neglected to share the most significant event of that day, so I will tell you now. As they said, it was a terrible day to fish, but we threw the nets anyway. Suddenly the boat began to rock, and Jesus told us to pull in our nets. To our amazement, they were loaded with fish, more than Zebedee's craft could handle. We had to drag them behind us to shore because they were too heavy to pull into the boat. It was a miracle, and how fitting it should happen on the day Jesus called us forth to fish for men.

It was a common thing for Jesus to bring James, John, and me away from the others to talk about the work. The three days on Mount Tabor were one of those times. John and James already reported their recollections of that retreat and how each of them was transformed by the Spirit of God. You need to know it was a profound experience for me as well.

As I listened to Jesus speak on that retreat, I kept envisioning our father Moses, who led our people out of captivity and into a new land of promise. That is what Jesus was doing, I realized. He was so filled with the Spirit of God as he spoke! Surely, Moses and the prophets approved of him and the work he was trying to do for our people. It was as though he were anointed to finish what they had started.

Salome reminded you of the words Jesus spoke to us when we broke bread together for the last time. The moment I remember most from that night was when Jesus washed our feet. When he came before me, I wanted to wash his feet, but he would not have it. "Peter," he said, "let me do this, for with this water you are made clean." Many of you at this memorial have told us about your moments of awakening. This was mine. It is the moment when Jesus became my Lord and Savior. I knew I was cleansed, ready to stand before God like an innocent babe, and then, as a man, ready to do the service to which he was calling me.

Dear friends, we are sad now, but we can look forward to the rich blessings God keeps for his people in the Heavenly Kingdom. Jesus has gone ahead of us. As we wait for that glorious day, we must be obedient to God's word just as Jesus was, not like those who are still ignorant.

I am afraid that with Jesus gone, the leaders in Jerusalem will try to take control again. But do not be deceived. Their authority does not come from God. They are waterless camels and do not understand mystery. Rather, turn to the apostles, the men whom Jesus chose to lead you.

In closing, let me remind you, dear brothers and sisters, that we need to be penitent and pray and the blessings of God will pour out upon us.

YAKOV

Peter, I thank you for your recollections. I have to say, however, I struggle with your thoughts that my brother's suffering was diminished by his sense of mission. You are trying to comfort my family, but what you say is not achieving that end. To us he was Yeshua, the boy who fought with his siblings, went to the synagogue, and traveled with us to Jerusalem for the holy days. He struggled, as each of us did, when our parents placed rules in his way. He did not stop being a human being when he stepped into his work. As John said, Yeshua was afraid, as any of us would have been, when he knew what was to come. Because he was human, he felt the pain when the soldiers' whips slashed his flesh. He felt the crush of the nails in his hands and feet. To diminish his suffering is to diminish the price he paid.

That is enough! I will not belabor my point.

Allow me to breathe, to return to the peace dwelling in our community here. Thank you, Father, Creator God.

Nathaniel is from Bethsaida, the birthplace of Peter, Andrew, and Philip. While Peter and Andrew became fishermen, Nathaniel and Philip became scholars. I met both of them when they spent time in Jerusalem. They went back to Bethsaida about the time Jesus returned from the East. Nathaniel, I know you will have much insight concerning some of the things that have been shared here today. Please come, dear brother.

NATHANIEL

I t is good we are here together to remember our brother, Jesus. Your brother in the flesh, Yakov, but ours in the oneness of the Spirit. What a blessing it has been thus far to hear the stories about how divine love transforms.

The manner in which I was inspired to follow Jesus was not as dramatic as some of the stories we have heard here. In a remote grove west of Bethsaida, Philip and I used to go to have discussions and to pray together. Sometimes other students came. One day, Philip came to me full of excitement to tell me about a rabbi he had met. "He is a master of the law," he said, "but his teachings go beyond what Moses taught us. He is able to get to the inner essence in ways I have never before heard." He told me he had heard this rabbi speak at the synagogue in Capernaum. "I know where to find him," he said.

I went with him, and we found Jesus at Peter's house.

He greeted me by name as though we were old friends. "How do you know me?" I asked him.

"Oh, I have been among those who gathered around to listen to you and the other students arguing about the law. I listened carefully to what you had to say, and I was very impressed." Needless to say, his special attention won me over. After that, I came to see all that Philip had said was true. Very quickly, Jesus opened my eyes to see everything in a new light.

Jesus refuted the old teachings concerning the Kingdom of God. He said its location is neither on a portion of land nor out there somewhere beyond the dome of the heavens. Rather, it is here, now, within each of us. We know this in our hearts, we see it with our inner eye, and once we see, it changes how we live and think.

This is an important teaching. You are in error, Peter, when you speak of the Kingdom to come in the future. It would be a great disservice to have our visitors leave with this misunderstanding. Jesus' intention was that we all know and see the Kingdom. This is not to say the Pharisaic belief in life after death is incorrect, but rather the Kingdom of God is truly present here among us now. We need not wait for it.

You heard Philip speak about being "attached to the mind." I was equally attached. I remember as a young man sitting with the other students and rabbis arguing my position concerning the law. Strangely, even as I spoke, I questioned my own words. Now I see I was caught in the contradiction between the God of judgment and a God of mercy. I think my true soul was trying to emerge, but I kept shoving it back into the darkness. I did this to hang on to the approval of others, I suppose. I don't know.

I remember a conversation I had with Jesus—it was soon after I agreed to go with him. I told him I wanted to experience the presence of God as surely as Moses did when he took off his sandals and walked on holy ground. Jesus looked at me and said, "Nathaniel, stop trying so hard to see something that is so close to you that it is *in* you. Look at me. You do not see a struggle, do you? Let go and see the light that is already there." Then he said, "Because the Spirit is in you, you do not need anyone to teach you. The Spirit is your teacher now." You see, the message of the inner teacher was first given to me by Jesus, and now I give it to you.

There are those who most remember Jesus as a healer. People often brought their sick family members to him with great hope and expectation. Jesus always stopped to spend time and pray with them. During those moments, so intense was Jesus' love and compassion and so complete the abandonment of the one seeking healing that it seemed there was a light moving back and forth between them. All else faded in comparison—the room, the trees, the people watching. For those moments in time, there was only Jesus and the one being healed. When it was over, it felt to me that even those watching were in some way healed.

When the disciples were alone together, Jesus spoke to us about healing. "The old teaching is that sickness of the body or of the mind is a result of sin. This is false," he said. "Illness is a condition of the earthly life. But all suffering can be used by God to awaken one to the Kingdom within. This is why one can be healed even when the manifestations of the illness do not change."

As for those who accused him of being an imposter or a magician, Jesus said, "The deeds I do are done in obedience to the Father. When people are healed, it is not me, but the Father who lives in me. Those who say these things do not understand because their eyes are not open."

I have spoken for a long time. Please forgive me. I know there are many yet who have something to say. These are the memories that fill my heart and soul today. Just because his body is not with us does not mean his Spirit is gone. The love we have for one another and the fact that hearts continue to change is proof he is here with us, just as he promised.

May we all continue to grow in the life awakened in us. I love you all. Thank you, dear ones.

YAKOV

Nathaniel, you are one of our great teachers. I thank you.

You made clear for us Jesus' message concerning the Kingdom of God on Earth and Peter's misunderstanding of the Kingdom to come in the future. You also spoke about healing. I cannot help but wonder—and only Peter and Perpetua can speak of this—if his trust in the Kingdom to come is a comfort, since their little Petronilla's body was not healed of palsy before Jesus was taken from us. I think you are correct in saying Jesus believed inner healing was as profound and true as healing of the body. But what does this mean for a child and the child's parents? I don't know about these things. It is very difficult.

Our journey this day began with a story by brother Matthew of new shoes and the poor table manners of Ammihud the tax collector. I think it is time to hear from his wife and companion, Arsinoe, whom James claims is the real reason Jesus allowed Matthew to come. Come, Arsinoe, and share some of your memories.

ARSINOE

My fondest memory of Jesus is of watching him walk among the sick and poor, among the families, getting to know them by name and listening to their stories. There was no aspect of their lives that did not capture him. When he saw there was a need, he would call upon us to assist. "Come, Suzanna, pray with me for this woman who grieves the loss of her child." "Bring your salve, Joanna, for the eyes of this man who cannot see." To Jude he'd say, "Come, brother, this man is controlled by a spirit. Tell him how you found freedom." "Philip, sit with these seekers and open the meaning of the Torah for them." This way he built the Kingdom. Salome calls it kneading the dough.

On the night of the Passover, Jesus washed our feet. Do you remember what he said when he was done? "This is meant to be an example for you," he said. "You are servants of the earth. You are caretakers, tenders, menders, healers, teachers, purifiers, planters, harvesters. Continue to serve one another as I have served you."

Yakov spoke so kindly about the women, and I am so grateful. We have been taught to serve by our mothers and grandmothers, just as the men have been taught by their fathers and grandfathers to lead. Jesus penetrated the veil between us. To the women he said, "Lead," and to the men he said, "Serve." And he penetrated the veil between the earthly kingdom and the Heavenly Kingdom. In the Kingdom of God each person is led by the Spirit, and each must pay attention. Jesus said, "The sheep know the shepherd's voice."

Now I want to tell you a thing or two about my husband. It is true he likes to color his stories a bit, but don't be fooled. Matthew has an acute sense of what is right and what is wrong, of who speaks from the heart and who speaks from . . . well, I won't tell you his words for people who speak only out of their sense of self-importance.

Matthew takes great pleasure in lifting the humble and lowering the haughty. Miriam told me this is why Jesus chose him. She said Jesus loved coming to our home. Matthew and I, in turn, loved having Jesus come because he never distinguished between rich and poor, sick and well, young and old, powerful and lowly. To each one he passed the cup with equal distinction. He looked into their eyes and saw only light.

When Jesus asked my husband and me to join him in his work, I felt loss when I abandoned my little kitchen. How could I know I would be feeding multitudes in the fields of Galilee? People were hungry to hear the message of Jesus, the good news that God is here dwelling among them, and we gave them bread so they would see that all he said is true. What a blessing these three years have been!

This past month in Capernaum has been dark. It has been difficult to find joy. But people are coming again to our table. Many have questions. They miss seeing Jesus walk the streets each day, visiting the merchants, breaking his bread with the beggars, and sharing tea with the masons and carpenters waiting for their workday to begin. We tell those who come to us what we have learned about the love of the Father and the Kingdom within. They don't always comprehend what we say, but we are learning to be patient with the Spirit.

Thank you, Mara, for the music and for the blessing of the children. This, too, is the Kingdom come on Earth.

YAKOV

The pictures you paint, Arsinoe, capture my brother Yeshua as I most remember him. This meandering among people was typical of him even as a small boy. Mother was always sending me to look for him and bring him home. I would find him in a field with the sheepherders or at the tanner's, rubbing his oily hands across the skins drying in the sun. He never wanted to come home with me until I told him our father had ordered it. I could see the beggar, the herder, the winemaker, the rabbi—whomever he was visiting—was sad to see him leave. "Come back again, Yeshua," they would say. "You are always welcome, Yeshua."

Thank you, Arsinoe. These memories are sweet morsels for me.

Now you will hear from another James from our community, this one the younger brother of Matthew. James came to be a disciple only during the last year of the campaign. I believe it was Miriam who encouraged him. Some of you have seen James's artistic work on the doors and gates on the finer houses in Bethsaida. Near the west gate there are statues of deer and raccoon and birds. The wagon that carries little Petronella around was made by James, and some of the drums you see about the platform are his.

James is a man of few words, but we ask him to open himself now and grace us with his wisdom.

JAMES, BROTHER
OF MATTHEW

Matthew is the one gifted with words, and I have always been content to be still. But now I must speak, for my heart is on fire as I stand here today.

I begin with a word of praise for my brother. Tax collectors are considered traitors and thieves among the people. You all know this. But I know Matthew counted every coin with justice in his heart. His home was modest, and he was always ready to give a poor beggar a coin or a place at his table. Arsinoe tells me she did not always know who would come through the door with her husband. Jesus was once a surprise visitor. But she accepted this because they are of one heart.

I am humbled by Yakov's words of praise for my work. I may not sound so humble, however, when I say I am just as pleased by the art I make as those who praise me, for it gives me great joy to present to the world something of use or of beauty. At the same time, I wonder where such gifts come from. How is it that one has an inclination to take a knife to a piece of wood or a chisel to a stone to form a bowl or an image?

In the beginning God took clay from the earth and formed a human being. When we take wood from the cypress to build a fence or wool from the sheep to weave a fine garment, we are doing what the Creator has done. This is the Creator's plan. God rested on the seventh day, but he set man to labor so that creation continues. Jesus said what we do is more than an imitation of God. It is the very act of God himself using us, his first creation, to continue the work he began. Remember, after man and woman were formed, God breathed his own Spirit, Ruach, into them.

God asks only one thing of us: to allow Ruach to flow. This is how God moved through Jesus. I recall a portion of his prayer after the love feast we shared before he died. Speaking to the Father, he said, "I gave them the same glory you gave me, in order that the world may know that you live in them." Jesus made the Father known through the vehicle of his gifts. It is our work now to use ours for the same purpose.

YAKOV

When this man of few words decides to speak, each word arrives on the wings of an eagle, it seems to me. I felt the presence of Yeshua himself as I watched and listened.

Brother Thomas is next. Thomas is a man of many words and is known to speak his mind. If something isn't working, he will tell you so. I have to admit it was often an irritation to me, but Yeshua welcomed his opinion. I have come to appreciate Thomas as I have gotten to know him more intimately these past weeks. Thomas, come and share your insights with us.

THOMAS

I find myself feeling something I have not felt since Jesus' death: zeal for the work. It seemed to have dissipated along with courage, for how can one feel courage in the face of the resistance and threats still coming out of Jerusalem? But now I am listening to these wonderful stories, these memories, and all sorts of emotions stir in me, including zeal. And joy. I feel the same joy I did when he walked with us in the flesh.

I realize as I listen that none of us knew the whole of Jesus. When we were gathered together, he was the teacher, the rabbi. But, as you have heard here today, there were in-between moments when his True Self encountered the True Self in one of us. These moments occurred all along the paths we traveled. As he spoke to each of us, it seemed he revealed different aspects of the Divine. It is as though each of us knows a secret we hold in our hearts. It reminds me of the parable of the treasure the farmer found in his field. It is worth more than anything we have been given. It is worth dying for.

There are a few things I want to share with you concerning the treasure given to me, but first I need to address the issue of our brother, Peter. I don't worry, as Nathaniel does, that what I say might offend Peter. When a man has a head as hard as a rock, you need to approach it with a chisel and hammer.

Some have called me a doubter, but I am not a doubter. I am one who knows to wait upon the truth. What Jesus taught me is that truths encountered without must be confirmed by the True Self within. When we act on that which cannot be confirmed, we are living a lie. This is the biggest complaint about the Sadducees. They believe they already have the truth, so they cease seeking the truth. It does not matter that their beliefs have the power to cause pain and havoc around them. They feel led to preach it anyway. If you challenge them, they cling to their truth as though it were a body part.

This is true of you, Peter. Even when a new truth is right in your face, you keep doing the same thing, speaking the same nonsense. You are as blind as a bat, and yet you want to lead others. If we let you go, you will lead the sheep over a cliff.

You like to imagine yourself as one in the inner circle

because Jesus so often brought you along with him. Open your eyes! He wanted you at his side so he could keep his eye on you. Peter, my brother, he gave you the keys to the Kingdom, but you have yet to open the door! If you did, you would not be telling people to go here or there to find the Kingdom, nor that is it being withheld from them until sometime in the future.

For me, the most important teaching Jesus gave us is this: "Know thyself." Your problem, Peter, is that you, as yet, do not know who Peter is. Jesus taught that those who do not know themselves do not know the Father. I pray for the day when you will open your eyes and see. I know this will happen because the Spirit of Jesus still works among us.

Suzanna, Jude, and James, son of Zebedee, I think your stories demonstrate exactly what I am talking about. Your encounters with Jesus sent you within. Seeing oneself in the light is at first troubling. But this is because the false self does not want to know the truth—that we are human beings capable of deception and of doing harm to others. To admit this, we believe, will bring upon us the wrath of God. But there is no wrath! There is only love! This is the meaning of the story of the prodigal son. Did the father berate the son for his sinful ways? No! He simply embraced him.

The cross. I don't want to think of it. I don't want to recall the nails in his hands and feet or see again the twisted look on his face. I want to wash away the memory of the blood pouring out from the wounds of the thorns. Oh, where was the Creator who gave this vessel to us? James, did the Divine Artist lose interest in his work?

This was my despair before I came here today. But I am coming to see now that while Jesus the man did not survive the cross, Love did survive. Those who stood at the foot of the cross have told us he managed to say in his anguish, "Father, forgive them." Can you believe such love? It makes me feel weak and small. I can only believe his words came from the Divine Self within him.

What a crowd we have here today! I think only the gathering at Bethsaida would compare. Some of you are hearing about him for the first time. I pray you can in some way come to know him as we know him. Then the True Self in you will have a story to tell. This is how it should be.

There is one more thing I want to share with you. Jesus spoke to us about his experience in the East. He loved the soul work being done by the *rashis.* These are wise men like the Jewish tsadikim. "They treated my soul like a garden," he told me. I asked him why he came home to Israel. He said, "My soul ached for humanity's children. They do not see how empty it is to live only in the earthly kingdom." Jesus and I had many talks about what he learned from his teachers. I have decided I myself want to follow in his footsteps and go there. Before he died, he wrote a letter of introduction for me to take. I plan to begin a journey to India after Shavuot. I hope you will pray for me.

We gather here in his name, and he is with us. Praise be to God.

YAKOV

The sun is getting lower in the sky, a sign we are getting closer to the end of our time together. Soon we will be building fires and setting set up camps for the night. Some of you will leave us, and we want to bless you before you go. But first we will hear from the two women closest to Yeshua, our mother, Mary, and his dearest friend, Miriam.

My mother, Mary, is the daughter of Joachim and Anna. It is through her that the priestly line comes to us, as Joachim did service in the Temple. She married my father, Joseph, God rest his soul, and they settled in Nazareth. My father, just as his father Heli before him, worked as a carpenter, taking on building projects wherever he could find them. They raised seven children in a small earthen home in Nazareth. You heard from our sister Mara and our brother Jude earlier. All the boys in our family accompanied our father as we grew into manhood. When his strength began to wane, we became the support of the family.

This past month has been difficult for my mother. I am glad she saw fit to be here. No one knows the child like the mother. Come, Mother, and share with us your reflections.

MARY

Miriam tells me I have been buried with Yeshua in the tomb. It feels like that—dark and cold and alone. When Yakov wanted to go ahead with the day of memorial, I fought him. "I am not ready," I pleaded.

"You will never be ready," he told me, "but life is ready for your return." My son is right. The light, though dim, is here once more. Thank you, Yakov, for not listening to your mother this one time.

I want to thank John for the hours he spent sitting with me, and attending to my needs this past month. Such a young man, yet he did not run from the rantings of a distressed woman. Suzanna says the evil spirits are finally growing weary of me. God knows I have grown weary of them. In these last few days, sleep is finally coming.

I so want to feel joy again. I want to experience the warmth of the sun and the sweet fragrance of lilies of the valley. I want to weave with woolen thread and hold my precious grandchild, Simeon, and run my fingers through his silken hear. I want to feel the rhythm of the drum and the rain on the roof of my house. I want to sing praises once again to the God I believe has been suffering with me. When I am free, perhaps God will stop weeping as well.

In the weeks since Yeshua's death, people have wanted to know about his birth and about his early years. Where does one begin?

God gave me a son, and what a fistful he was, always questioning. I will tell you one little story, and it is true. When my husband, Joseph, God rest his soul, took the boys to the synagogue as a good Jewish father should, Yeshua was ever restless. One day, during the recitation of the psalms, Joseph looked down and noticed Yeshua with a stick in hand, drawing in the sand on the floor. He said he felt he should stop him and insist he sit up like the older boys. "But he was quiet," Joseph said, "and down there the rabbi could not see him."

After prayers were completed, Joseph knelt to see Yeshua had drawn a picture of a house. He asked whose house it was, and Yeshua said, "It is God's house."

"Oh," Joseph said, "you have drawn a picture of the Temple in Jerusalem."

"No," Yeshua said. "God doesn't live there anymore." Joseph was startled and slightly amused. He told me he looked around to see if the rabbi was near. Then he asked Yeshua in a whisper, "Why did God move out of the Temple?" and Yeshua replied, "Because the people can't see him there." Do you see how smart he was, even then?

I suspect, Thomas, you were much like Yeshua when you were small. If I could share tea with your mother, God rest her soul, I am sure she would tell me a mother's stories of a curious little boy. In the early mornings I have seen you go out to greet the sun as it comes up in the East. Yeshua used to do this, and when he left us, I wondered if it was the sun he was seeking. It is right that you go on your journey, Thomas. May the God of light who guided my son guide you as well.

James, thank you for your insights about the work of the artist. As I listened to your words it occurred to me that when we share in the work of the Creator, we grow attached to the work. Yeshua was my work. All of my children are my work, but Yeshua required more of me than the others. The words that came out of my mouth more often with him than with any others were, "Listen to me!" It always seemed as if someone else was telling him what to do, and he had to consider my requests in this light. Joseph, God rest his soul, used to say to me, "Our children are not our own. Their father is the One in Heaven, and it is he whose will they must follow."

I thought when Joseph grew ill Yeshua would change

his mind about leaving, but he did not. And my husband did not deter him. "He needs to be about the Heavenly Father's work," he told me. "He needs to go away to find out what that work is."

Letting go is the task of the parent, and I fear I am not very good at it. I thought when Yeshua left to do his seeking I had let him go, but clearly I did not, for when he returned and did not remain in Nazareth my heart broke once again. At the cross, God asked me to let him go back to where he came from, back into the dark womb, back into the arms of his Creator. It was more than I could bear. I was clinging too hard, and my clinging was to the dreams I had for Yeshua—not God's dreams, but my own.

There was a tension between Yeshua and me during the early days of his work. "I am a man who knows what to do," he said to me. That was *his* truth. I told him, "You did not allow me the luxury of watching you change. You left as one person and came home another. Give me time to get accustomed to this new man." This was *my* truth.

I remember he laughed when I said that. "I am not as crazy a man as I appear, Mother," he said. "Behind every word and action there is a higher purpose. The Spirit of God has come to dwell in me."

That is when he asked me to come along with him. "Clopas and Mara are coming. They can use your help watching Simeon. There will be other children as well."

That became my role, the tender of the lambs. And the little lambs, more than anything Yeshua said, awakened my soul to the Kingdom.

Miriam, when Yeshua left for the East, you were just a child, thin as a reed, a little girl who preferred to climb trees and chase rabbits rather than cook and weave. When we stayed at your family's home in Bethany you used to follow him around like a puppy to get his attention. When we left he complained about how annoying you were. But after his travels he found you transformed into a woman, and he was not so annoyed. When he asked you to come along with us, it was an invitation to walk beside him—not to follow him like a puppy jumping for attention—as the support he knew he would need to do the Father's work. He called you Mariameme, his tower of strength.

So, you want to know the message of the mother? Much wisdom has been shared here today, and I don't know what more I could add.

Life did not turn out as I thought when I was a young girl, but it is the life set before me. I have had to face many things I would rather not have put into the design of my life. Sadness is a new talis for me. I think I will have to wear it for as long as I live on this earth.

With age comes wisdom, the child of pain and joy. Wisdom sees cause and effect. Wisdom sees that darkness will return and light will return. It perceives the cycle of things. Wisdom sees that knowing the truth about oneself sets one free. This is what I gather from these testimonies today. One cannot awaken without truth, and truth is hard. "The stone which the builders rejected as worthless turned out to be the most important of all. This is the work of the Lord," we sing, "what a wonderful sight it is!"

I feel Yeshua's hand upon me.

YAKOV

You heard our mother say when she spoke of her husband, Joseph, "God rest his soul." Jews use these words when remembering our loved ones. These are words of hope. We ask the God of mercy to bring our loved ones into a place of rest, not torment as some believe. I imagine this rest to mean contentment or satisfaction that one has lived a life pleasing to the Father. I know my father rests knowing the woman he cared for and who shared his life and bed is revered among the people for her love and wisdom. He rests knowing his children are bearing fruit and doing the work our Father in Heaven asks of them. He rests knowing Judah has returned. When we last gathered together at the Passover meal, Jesus spoke of the place of rest. Joseph, the humble carpenter, has already discovered it. He has welcomed his son, and they will welcome us.

I know that, had my father been here when Jesus returned from the East, he would have given his heart and labor to the work.

And now our dear sister Miriam speaks. As Jesus' confidante, she knew him better than any of us. They were of one Spirit, of one mind and heart. They prayed together. Together they sat in silence, meditating on the Great Mystery. If Jesus had any doubts and fears, I know he shared them with Miriam. He told her things he did not share with the others. I pray now that the time of sheloshim is past, she will step forward and teach us these things. We await her guidance.

MIRIAM

This is a sacred place where we come together. It is holy ground where we rest and tell our stories and listen to one another. My soul sings today, and my Spirit rejoices. It sings a song of love, the love of our beloved one here yet in our midst. Jesus has shed the earthly body and is free now to do great things in us as he promised.

Yakov, Jesus knew you. He knew your heart was divided and that soon you would find your way. He held a place for you, and now he has told you himself what he wants of you, to serve as our leader. And for Peter there was a word, too. It appears the rock Thomas saw in your head, Jesus calls a stepping stone. Have no fear, for you will have your day to lead.

These two Jesus saw as leaders, but he had plans for all of us, for it was not his will that the message of the Kingdom of God within should die. The Kingdom is alive and here, and we must all bring others forth into it. We are all one Shepherd.

Mary told you about the times when her family would stay with us in Bethany during Passover. She is right that I used to follow Jesus like a pup and pester him for any crumb that might fall from his table.

Who is to say what drew me to Jesus more than the other boys? A child feels. Her spirit is moved, but she does not think about such things. I favored him—this is all I know. When he was gone I did not think of him. But when he was there, I always turned to him as though a common thread tied us together. When he went to the East and his family came to Bethany without him, I noticed the gap and a small yearning started to grow in me.

I remember that day, years later, when he came through the door of our house. Lazarus dropped what he was doing and ran to embrace him. Jesus was smiling and talking, but he suddenly looked up and saw me. "Who is this?" he said. I knew he knew me, but not the woman I had become. For that moment, I thanked God for making me pleasant to look at.

Later, he and Lazarus were sitting at table with some of the men from the synagogue. I sat on the floor near Jesus to listen to what he had to say, once again like a puppy. Well, he stopped in the middle of his own sentence and turned and looked at me. "Miriam, come in," he said. The men thought he was inviting me into the circle, which would have shocked them. But I grasped fully what he meant. He was saying, "Come into the Kingdom." So I stepped in. It was easy. It was like coming into my true home.

So, I went with him, and you became my new family. Who could have known what was in store for us as we walked out together into the byways and towns of Galilee? Who among you storytellers knew what Jesus would awaken in you?

On the night of the feast, do you remember how our hearts were full of joy? It was a Passover he wanted to share with us. We were all there, the workers and their families, his own family and friends and the children. So many who are here today again!

And after it was over, he brought only the disciples with him to the garden of Gethsemane, where we had gone many times to pray and rest. We were full of good food and tired. His words at the table were still swirling around, waiting for our hearts to take hold of them. He had spoken about leaving us and the suffering to come, but in the peaceful quiet of the night, having him still with us, we felt safe and calm.

Jesus had spoken to me many times about death, yet even I was not ready for the horror to come. "I do not want to go," he told me. "They are precious to me, and they are not ready to live fully the Kingdom within." He was talking about all of you and about those who had come to hear his message.

I tried to console him. "They will grow to become tillers of each other's soil."

But that night he confessed to all of us his fear. "Please don't leave me," he pleaded. And yet he went off alone.

There were many things that worried Jesus. "They are still bound by false teachings," he told me. "Sin keeps trying to capture them and pull them away. They don't understand how simple it is." He told me all that is asked is that we each live by our highest nature: "Then sin falls away like dust from your shoes. Live by your lower nature, and you are walking in mud."

It was Jesus' desire that we not live in fear or discord. This is the message he gave us during our meal together. "Be at peace," he said. "Be content in your heart knowing the Father is watching over you. You have everything you need. Receive gladly all that is good, and let go of all that is contrary to good."

Dear ones, I feel your distress. I see your tears. I hear your fears when you say, "How are we going to go out into the world to spread the good news about the Kingdom of God? If the powers did not spare Jesus, they certainly will not spare us." What you say is probably true, but if we hold back, what will become of the sheep?

Do not let your hearts be troubled, for Jesus prepared

a place for us. He tended his garden with all the love and energy he could muster. Weeding, he helped us overcome our human weaknesses while he transformed them into the keys that opened the door to the Kingdom. Pay attention to what I am saying! This is the testimony you have heard today: every moment of anguish speaks to the anguish of each of us; every moment of awakening speaks hope to those who still seek.

I was asked to tell you what Jesus spoke to me alone. I do this gladly, for there is nothing hidden from those who open their hearts. He taught about the things that keep a person from rising above the earthly kingdom. There are three hindrances, he said.

The first is darkness. It is the spirit of darkness that pursued Jesus himself. Why do you think he could reach down into the soul of a man or woman? Jesus told me that when he went out on his search for the wisdom of the Eastern fathers, he got lost in the wilderness. He knew little about surviving on wild plants or how to protect himself from the demons of the night. "I came face-to-face with fear," he told me. "Fear of starvation, fear of failure, fear of being alone and unloved, fear of having no purpose." He said he considered death as the only escape and came close to throwing himself from the precipice. But then he sat down and entered deeply into that thought. "Suddenly," he said, "I realized the darkness had left me."

When one lives in darkness, it seems like there is no place to go. One does not turn to the light because darkness is all one knows. Some of you know what this feels like, for you have been there. It is only love that can penetrate such darkness. And we must know that love will be repelled at first. Never stop, dear ones, when you see someone in darkness. And don't let your ego tell you that you are the only source of another's light. There are others. If you offer love and are rejected, send another. You may judge that the light in your brother or sister seems less bright than yours, but it may be the only light a person in darkness can see.

The second hindrance that keeps one from rising above the earthly kingdom is desire. No one knows better than I how desire keeps us blind. When Jesus died, I thought my own self had died.

What animated my body those hours, I do not know, but I went dutifully to the tomb with herbs and balm. I was hoping when I arrived I would find the tomb empty—that it had all been a dream. I know I was denying what my soul knew to be true. I just wanted to touch him again and to hear his voice. I wanted to look into his eyes and see not the eyes of anguish, but the eyes that smiled at little children, the eyes that lifted to the Father in prayer, the eyes that looked upon me.

I know that Jesus yielded willingly! I thought as I approached the tomb. *Did he not think of what this would do to the heart of his beloved?* Yet this very thing, this total surrender, is what made me want to follow him in the first place. I sat pondering these things at the opening of the tomb. *How can I go about this earthly life? How am I to take one step and then another?* I cried out, "Why did you forsake me?"

Then I heard a voice. "Miriam," it said. I looked up to see an old man with a hoe in his hand. He was looking into my soul in the same way Jesus used to do. "Do not cling to him," he said. "The body was just a garment he wore. If you cling to it, you will not see him." Then I remembered that Jesus had said, "I will always be with you." That is when desire left me, for desire teaches us that there is never enough. "There is more to be had," desire says. "There is more needed to make you happy." I realized I have all I need.

Jesus was among us as our teacher. Others have already told you he liked to use his gift of metaphor to help the people understand. "The Kingdom of God is like this thing, or that," he would say. Like a rock, a tree, a bug, a flower, a gem. He taught by his life as well. He touched the untouchables to show us no one is untouchable. He went into fearful places to show us we need not fear. He spoke the truth when truth would lead to danger to show us truth will set us free. He brought life to his words. He asked that we not just listen with our ears but also imitate him in our actions.

But the center of his teaching was not his teaching at all. The center was the Spirit to be transmitted. He breathed into us his own Spirit. See and believe! When you love, when you know, when you choose good over evil, it is the same Spirit that dwelt in him, the Anointed One. Because we receive the same Spirit, we too are anointed and become one with God and with one another.

The third hindrance to realizing the Kingdom is ignorance. I told you Jesus understood darkness and was able to see it in others. But he said, "I do not judge those who don't recognize me. I recognize them, and I know those things of the earth that they believe in will come to an end. Then they will see." Jesus understood the world in which we are all planted and in which we grow. Concerning ignorance he said, "They believe what they have been told about themselves and about God. This is true of all, not just the children of Israel. Whether male or female, Greek or Roman, wealthy or poor, whole or infirm . . . it matters not. There are many false shepherds eager to lead them astray."

Be like him, dear ones, and do not judge. Simply see and understand. Know that those false teachings the ignorant ones believe in are of no spiritual substance. Speak truth, and even your little bit of truth will set them free. Tell your story. It is what the Father has given you.

Jesus also revealed to me that even after we open our eyes to see the Kingdom within, we will continue to struggle with the powers of this earthly place. Listen to all that has been said here today and know this truth. We continue to struggle to understand spiritual things. We continue to judge one another. Love has barely taken root. Weeds abound in our garden. At times we conform to the wisdom of the earthly kingdom. Alas, my soul!

But we dare not lose heart! I stand before you, and I can feel him present. His Spirit moves between the Heavenly Kingdom and the earthly kingdom, through you to me. We are one with him and with one another.

"My kingdom come on Earth as it is in Heaven," he prayed. Let us make this our prayer, dear ones, and our mission.

Oh, sing my soul, sing!
What bound me has been loosed.
Darkness has dissipated.
Desire has reached its end.
I am free from ignorance.
I am free.

YAKOV

Yes, as Miriam told you, Jesus came to me in spirit and spoke the words as she said. But, my friends, do not be impressed by this. Teachers are judged by stricter rules than others. And besides this, I am not a master but a helper. This is what he meant when he washed our feet. This is how we live in the Kingdom of God, not the earthly kingdom. I beg of you, do not forget this as we go forward.

Let me tell you another thing Jesus said to me when he came in spirit. I tell you because it is a truth not just for me, but for you as well.

He said, "Know yourself and love yourself."

"How do I love myself?" I asked.

"Act toward yourself as I myself act toward you," he said.

This was an amazing thing for me to hear. I had to

think deeply about all the ways my brother acted toward me. I was amazed. He treated me with more kindness and love than I ever afforded myself.

You have heard testimony today, stories of Jesus' disciples coming to know the truth about their own selves. Why this teaching? Because Jesus understood that the True Self is one with God, and to know one is to know the other.

So you see, this same hope is for all of us, the beloved community and also all of you who came to be with us today. Many of you knew him as a friend or neighbor. Some were healed by him; some experienced forgiveness of sins because of him. No matter. The gift he offers of his own Spirit is for all. Receive and be changed.

When he opened my mind to understanding, Jesus told me, "Walk correctly." By this he meant, "Put into practice what is given to you, or it will die." I say the same to you. Submit to God. Accept the word he plants in your heart, but don't just listen and walk away: put it into practice. Act! Don't be afraid, for God will bless you in all you do.

What do I mean by action? These words come from a priest who serves in the Temple, who knows the law and rituals and practices all with a faithful heart. It is this very same priest who says to you now that if you want to practice a pure and genuine religion, care for the orphans and widows, and treat people with respect regardless of their wealth or poverty. Do not judge. God has shown us that mercy triumphs over judgment. In caring for the poor, don't just pray for them—that is what the priests in the Temple would do. Instead, attend to their needs as well. Feed them. Keep them warm.

The road ahead will not be easy. We don't know what has become of the forces that caused our beloved one's death. But we must not let worry weaken our faith. You have just a little faith you say? I say put that little faith into action and it will grow strong. We must not let the Kingdom of God wither away!

The character of the Heavenly Kingdom is pure, first of all, but it is also peaceful, gentle, and friendly. It is full of compassion and produces a harvest of good deeds. It is free from prejudice, criticism, and hypocrisy. This is not the character of the earthly kingdom that we walk in with our earthly bodies. Be filled with the Spirit of God and open your hearts! Jesus said to us, "Be always aware of the distinction between the two kingdoms, and always choose the higher one."

As this day comes to a close, already I dread our parting. When we gather, I feel the love of Jesus poured into us through the Holy Spirit. If you do not feel that, I pray the Spirit will come down upon you and fill you, first of all, and then overflow so the world may know He lives. The words do not matter, do they? Everyone understands love no matter the language they speak.

I will extinguish the fire we lit at the start of our ceremony, but already I see the fires burning about the camp. Furthermore, I see the fire burning in all of you.

AWAKEN!

LIST OF CHARACTERS

In the order they appear in the book:

Yakov (Hebrew for Jacob or James): The brother of Jesus. Yakov was not one of Jesus' followers while Jesus lived, but experienced a conversion after his death. He was chosen by Jesus to lead the community in Jerusalem. Referred to in the scriptures as "James the Just," he was a priest and served in the Temple in Jerusalem. In *Memorial of Jesus*, he leads the memorial service and introduces each of the disciples.

Matthew: A tax collector from Capernaum. Matthew and his brother James, also a disciple, are sons of Alpheus. In the gnostic writings, Matthew defended Mary Magdelene (Miriam) against Peter. Because of his defense of women, I had Matthew married to a strong woman, Arsinoe, who was one of the female disciples.

James: Son of Zebedee and Salome. James was referred to as "James the Greater," probably to distinguish him from Matthew's brother James.

Andrew: Andrew and his brother, Peter, grew up in Bethsaida. As an adult, he lived with Peter and his wife in Capernaum, where both worked as fishermen for Zebedee. Both brothers were followers of John the Baptist.

Suzanna: One of several women of wealth who helped Jesus' movement financially. Suzanna is said to have been healed of spirits and became one of the seven women who followed Jesus.

Simon: Called "Simon the Patriot," he was a close friend of Judas (who betrayed Jesus). Simon and Judas were both zealots, a more militant group of resistors to Roman rule.

Philip: Friend of Nathaniel. Both were rabbinic students. Philip is the author of the gnostic *Gospel of Philip*. He grew up in Bethsaida with Peter and Andrew.

Mara: Jesus' sister, Mary. I altered her name to distinguish her from the other Marys. She was married to Clopus, who was named in Luke's gospel as one of two disciples who met Jesus on the road to Emmaus.

Jude: Jesus' younger brother, also known as Judas. In the New Testament, he is sometimes refered to as Thaddaeus. Jude authored *The Letter of Jude*. The Church deemed him to be the saint of desperate causes.

John: Son of Zebedee and Salome and younger brother of James. Referred to as the "Beloved Disciple." In the gnostic text *Pistis Sophia*, John is referred to as "The Virgin." One scholar suggests that he was the delivery boy for his father's fishing business and would have been allowed into Caiaphas' home after Jesus' arrest.

Salome: Jesus' aunt. Salome was the wife of Zebedee the fisherman, mother of James and John, and the sister of Mary, Jesus' mother. Jesus often ate at Salome's table in Capernaum. She was one of the seven women disciples who followed him from Galilee to Jerusalem and participated in preparing Jesus' body for burial.

Joanna: Wife of Chuza. Chuza was the household administrator for Herod Antipas. They lived near Magdela.

Peter: Peter's actual name was Simon, but Jesus nicknamed him "Cephas," meaning "rock." He lived in Capernaum with his wife and family in a house not far from the shore where Zebedee docked his boats. Peter and his brother Andrew were followers of John the Baptist. Jesus lived in Peter's house when he settled in Capernaum. Peter and his wife, Perpetua, had a daughter, Petronella, who was affected by palsy. Peter healed her after Jesus' death.

Nathaniel: A pious Jewish contemplative and rabbinic student. Nathaniel was from the town of Cana, not far from where Jesus grew up in Nazareth. Nathaniel was best friends with Philip, and both were followers of John the Baptist.

Arsinoe: *The Revelation of James* names Arsinoe as one of the seven women followers of Jesus. Without much information to be found, she became Matthew's wife in this story.

James: Son of Alpheus, brother of Matthew. Called "James the Lesser", perhaps because he was younger or smaller in stature than James, the son of Zebedee. James was from Capernaum.

Thomas: Author of the gnostic *Gospel of Thomas*. Known as "The Disciple Who Doubted." Tradition says that he married at twenty-nine and had four children. Thomas started out as a carpenter, later turned to stone masonry, and eventually became a fisherman. Thomas is also called "The Twin" either because he literally was a twin or because of his similarity in character to Jesus. Thomas was from Tiberius.

Mary: Jesus' mother, wife of Joseph, but a widow during Jesus' public ministry. Sources suggest that she had a trade to support herself, but disagree upon whether she was a hairdresser or a weaver of cloth.

Miriam: Also known as Mary Magdeline. "Magdeline," from the Hebrew word *migdal*, means "tower." Scholars suggest this a reference to her status or her strong personality. Miriam was Jesus' companion and confidante. Some sources suggest that she was Mary of Bethany, sister of Martha and Lazarus. Miriam is an alternative name for Mary, and was chosen to distinguish her from the other Marys in the story.

DISCUSSION QUESTIONS

1. The book's characters include seventeen disciples who were chosen by Jesus to help carry his message about the Kingdom of God throughout the land of Israel. Each disciple shares a story of a very personal encounter with Jesus. For some, entering the Kingdom was difficult, but Jesus somehow broke through their barriers and opened their eyes.

Do you find similarities between any one particular character's story and your own? How do you feel about the way Jesus helped that character?

2. Though the seven women were not mentioned in the New Testament, their names can be found in non-canonical writings.

How do you feel about the portrayal of these women and their relationship with Jesus? Does it alter the way you think about ministry and leadership?

3. The memorial service takes place thirty days after Jesus' death, yet there is no mention of Jesus' resurrection. Nevertheless, the disciples spoke about Jesus' presence among them as though he were very much alive.

Andrew said, "They took his body but his Spirit remains."

Nathaniel said "Just because his body is not with us does not mean that his Spirit is gone."

Mary said, "I feel Yeshua's hand upon me."

Miriam said, "The Beloved One (is) here in our midst."

How do you feel about the author's way of presenting the resurrection? Do you find it more or less relevant?

4. In the second chapter, "James, son of Zebedee," Jesus confronts James about his treatment of his younger brother. This is a conversion experience that involves facing the truth about one's actions, true remorse, and making an amends.

Is James's experience similar or different from what you have understood about conversion?

5. What were some experiences in the stories that emphasize either the human nature or the divine nature of Jesus? Think of some other books or movies that depict the life of Jesus. Have these tended more toward presenting the divinity of Jesus or his humanity? Do you have a preference and why?

6. A central theme of the book is the Kingdom of God as within, rather than "out there," and as something that exists in the present moment.

Is this in agreement with what you have been taught about the Kingdom of God? What signs do you see that the

Kingdom of God is among us today?

7. Miriam said, "The Kingdom is alive and here and we must all bring others into it. We are all One Shepherd." Read the following poem by Teresa of Avila (1515-1582). How do her words and those of Miriam speak to Christians today?

> *Christ Has No Body*
> *Christ has no body but yours,*
> *No hands, no feet on earth but yours,*
> *Yours are the eyes with which he looks*
> *Compassion on this world,*
>
> *Yours are the feet with which he walks to do good,*
> *Yours are the hands, with which he blesses all the world.*
> *Yours are the hands, yours are the feet,*
> *Yours are the eyes, you are the body.*
> *Christ has no body now but yours,*
> *No hands, no feet on earth but yours,*
> *Yours are the eyes with which he looks*
> *compassion on this world.*
> *Christ has no body now on earth but yours.*

BIBLIOGRAPHY

Borg, Marcus J. *Meeting Jesus for the First Time: The Historical Jesus and the Heart of Contemporary Faith*. New York: HarperOne, 1994.

Bourgeault, Cynthia. *The Meaning of Mary Magdalene: Discovering the Woman at the Heart of Christianlty*. Boston: Shambhala, 2010.

Bourgeault, Cynthia. *The Wisdom Jesus: Transforming the Heart and Mind—A New Perspective of Christ and His Message*. Boston: Shambhala, 2008.

Hone, William. *Everyday Life in Biblical Times*. Washington D.C. National Geographic Society.

Hone, William. *Lost Books of the Bible*. Old Saybrook: Konecky & Konecky, 1926.

Meyer, Marvin. *The Nag Hammadi Scriptures: The Revised and Updated Translation of Sacred Gnostic Texts*. New York: HarperOne, 2007.

Notovich, Nicolas. *The Unknown Life of Jesus Christ.* Radford: Wilder Publications, LLC, 2008.

Pagels, Elaine. *The Gnostic Gospels.* New York: Random House, 1979.

Smith, Andrew Philip. *The Lost Sayings of Jesus: Teachings from Ancient Christian, Jewish, Gnostic and Islamic Sources—Annotated & Explained.* Woodstock: Skyline Paths Publishing, 2006.

Spong, John Shelby. *Rescuing the Bible from Fundamentalism: A Bishop Rethinks the Meaning of Scripture.* San Francisco: HarperSanFrancisco, 1992.

Tabor, James D. and Jacobovici, Simcha. *The Jesus Discovery: The New Archaeological Find That Reveals the Birth of Christianity.* New York: Simon & Schuster, 2012.

ABOUT THE AUTHOR

Judy Jeub grew up in Chicago, but prefers the country life of middle Minnesota so that she can greet the sun in her pajamas with a cup of coffee in hand. She received a degree in religious studies from Edgewood College in Madison, Wisconsin, and worked for ten years in religious education.

After attending St. Cloud University, she had a second career as a parent educator, which, she says, "prepared her to be a grandparent." Her passion is writing, especially stories of ordinary people. She also writes a blog where she can express her opinions about such things as politics, religion, and critters that visit her yard.

She enjoys reading, needlework, and likes to put the last piece in the puzzle that her husband, Bernie, labored over for weeks. She and her husband enjoy traveling, gardening, preserving the produce together, and spending time with their four children and their partners, twenty-three grandchildren, and six great-grandchildren.